TECHNIQUES
FOR
EFFICIENT RESEARCH

TECHNIQUES
FOR
EFFICIENT RESEARCH

by

LEWIS E. LLOYD, Sc.D.

Director of Business Research

The Dow Chemical Company

CHEMICAL PUBLISHING COMPANY, INC.

New York

1966

Q
180
·AIL55
1966
Cap.2

Printed in the United States of America

Preface

The need for increased productivity in scientific research is generally recognized. Mounting costs of research require constantly greater output "just to stay even," while at the same time the potential leverage which research can give to profits beckons toward even greater commitment to it. Many researchers, old and young, have not learned to apply good techniques. As a result of all this, efficient research, like the weather, is more talked about than improved.

The problem of how to employ good techniques as an aid to efficient research came to my attention when I was a young researcher. I first noticed my own lack of skill and then observed that many of my colleagues were as poorly equipped as I was in techniques for solving problems. At that time I questioned half a hundred Ph.D.'s in chemistry, physics, and engineering from a broad cross section of nationally recognized universities. In this group there was not one who had received organized instruction in how to do research. Moreover, a search of the literature revealed no report which treated this important question with adequate breadth and depth. There were statements on what is the scientific method but no directions on how to apply it. What is needed is renewed attention to the methodology of research—an answer to the question: How does one do research efficiently?

There was at hand no ready-made answer, but diligent search and study clarified the meaning of the scientific method and resulted in a logical and effective procedure that could be stated in a stepwise sequence. Although the procedure is based on the scientific method, it proved necessary to add steps and detail, which, although implied in the scientific method, have never before been directly stated. The problem-solving procedure is proposed specifically as a technique in research, but it is broad enough to fit any type of *problem*.

Further study of the question of efficiency in research revealed factors other than problem-solving which were of importance. This led to an examination of all aspects of the management of research. The latter chapters of this book will be of special interest to management, but they will also be of interest to the researcher himself, in that it will help him to visualize his own relationship to the total program.

This book is not designed as a philosophy of research. Rather, it seeks specific answers to the HOW questions:

> How does one do what one ought to do?
> How does one assemble facts?
> How does one arrange them in an orderly fashion?
> How can creativity be improved?

This is, in a sense, a "do-it-yourself" manual for self-improvement in the selection of problems and in solving them. The examples are largely taken from the chemical industry, but the principles are broadly applicable to all types of problems. The first part of the book is concerned primarily with the problem of solving problems; the second part is directed to problems of research management.

I especially wish to express my gratitude to Dr. John J. Grebe, formerly Director of Nuclear and Basic Research at the Dow Chemical Company (now retired), for the inspiration of his example and the insight that I have gained from our many discussions through the years, not only on the philosophy and methods of research but also on a wide variety of research problems. I also owe a debt of gratitude to the many researchers on industrial psychology from whose work I have borrowed.

I wish also to say thank you to Miss Lois Hoerlein for her valued assistance in preparing the manuscript.

August 1965   LEWIS E. LLOYD

Contents

chapter 1

INTRODUCTION

"A research man with a new problem should go to the laboratory first."

"Wouldn't it be better if he first went to the library to see what has already been done in the field?"

"Most certainly not!"

"Why?"

"Because whatever is in the literature will only prejudice the researcher and inhibit the application of his own fresh ingenuity to the problem."

"But I take the other stand. If the research worker does not go to the library first, he will waste much time repeating work already done and reported by others."

Such was part of a conversation between two experienced research workers who were discussing problem-solving methods at lunch one day. They were concerned about the more general problem of research efficiency and how to improve it. This was an unusual discussion, in one sense, because relatively little attention has been given to this problem. Billions of dollars are spent on research to improve efficiency in production and distribution, and more billions to find new products; but very little to improve the efficiency of research itself.

Perhaps this should not be surprising. The research man is too busy applying his scientific skill to fascinating problems to leave much time for developing better methods and tools. Moreover, engineers and physical scientists are sometimes baffled by problems of human relations. As they are inclined to expect people to behave logically, they are all too often unprepared for the emotionally directed behavior that is charac-

1

teristic of us humans. Management, to be sure, is concerned with personnel problems, but generally is not acquainted with the research worker's special problems. Thus, caught in the middle, methodology in research including the problem of *problem-solving* has not received the attention that it deserves.

Much Interest in R & D

That there is interest in the problem of efficient research is demonstrated by the many published papers with such titles as: "Research Management", "Research Organization", "Capitalizing on Research", or simply, "Research". There have also been many books written, particularly on industrial research. Some of these are statements of the philosophy of research by recognized leaders in the field of research. In others the authors have interviewed the research directors in various companies, or collected data and comments by questionnaire. By studying and summarizing such information, they have indicated what they believe to be the accepted practice in the more progressive laboratories. Finally, there is the book called *Handbook of Research Management*,[1] which is a series of chapters written, for the most part, by various consultants on different aspects of management of research. The reader must judge for himself how much is subtle advertising and how much is pet theory of the given consultant. To a large extent, however, this literature has indicated only what ought to be done, not how to do it; it has stated the objective, not the method.

It is the purpose of this book to focus attention on the *how* problem—the techniques for improving efficiency in research. This is not, however, a treatise on time-and-motion studies in the laboratory. Such studies, however worthy, have been effectively covered elsewhere both for the general subject and for the laboratory experimental techniques. We are concerned with the broader, more fundamental aspects of research procedure; with factors of organization and policy, and with the mental processes involved. It is in these areas that great strides in research efficiency can be made.

---

[1] Edited by Carl Heyel; Reinhold Publishing Corporation, New York, 1959.

Efficiency Is Important

Analysis of the problem reveals the major factors that affect efficiency in research. Once the problem has been broken down into its parts, each part can be examined step by step. Some factors involve primarily the research worker, and others, primarily management. The first part of this book examines ways in which the researcher himself can improve his own efficiency. Here are discussed the basic and important factors of creativity and problem-solving. The scientific method is elaborated in detail, and suggestions on how best to apply it are presented.

In the later chapters, attention is given to the importance of selecting a worthwhile problem and some criteria for the selection. Other factors of importance to effective organization and management of research are also discussed, always with the *how* question in mind.

Management everywhere seems to be concerned about trying to increase efficiency in research. Does this mean that research is less efficient than it ought to be? Are there substantial gains to be made, and if so, how? These and other questions need to be answered, not only because research is big business but also because, for twentieth-century America, research has become the Aladdin's lamp from which fabulous new things come by application of enough "polish." Practical businessmen look to research for new products and growth. National defense depends heavily on research for more effective weapons. Universities are rated by their accomplishments in research. We do research on everything from the atomic nuclei to galaxies, from the subconscious mind to rocks, from modern politics to ancient civilizations. Even grade-school children call it "research" when they go to the library. Our whole society is "research conscious".

EXPENDITURES FOR RESEARCH

The company executive no longer asks himself whether to *have* research; merely, "*How much* research?" He does not ask himself, "Can we afford research?"; he knows he cannot afford to be without it. No president would admit that his company was doing no research. In fact, this is the one part of the pro-

TABLE 1:1

EXPENDITURES FOR SCIENTIFIC RESEARCH

(millions of dollars)

Year[1]	Total Scientific Research Expend.	Industry[2]		Nonprofit Industrial Research Institutes	Government (Fed., State)	Colleges, Universities	Research Institutes
		Reported by V. Bush	Revised Est. by Y. Brozen				
1921	72.0e	29.4	48	—	12.0e	10.6e	1.0e
1922	84.0e	37.4	59	—	13.0e	11.0e	1.0e
1923	97.0e	44.0	70	—	14.0e	12.0e	1.0e
1924	110.6e	50.0	80	—	15.6	13.0e	2.0e
1925	124.3e	58.0	92	—	16.3	14.0e	2.0e
1926	138.0e	64.0	102	—	18.0	15.0e	3.0e
1927	147.9e	70.0	112	—	16.9	16.0e	3.0e
1928	158.0e	75.9	120	—	17.1	17.0e	4.0e
1929	181.0e	88.0	140	—	17.7	18.0e	5.0e
1930	217.0e	106.0	170	—	22.8	19.0e	5.0e
1931	235.0r	116.0	186	0.5	24.0	20.3	5.2
1932	268.0e	131.3	214	1.2	26.9	22.0	5.2
1933	277.0r	120.0	207	0.9	40.0	24.8	5.1
1934	231.0e	110.2	176	0.7	30.0e	20.0e	4.8
1935	244.0r	124.0	198	1.5	22.2	19.2	4.7
1936	269.0e	136.0	217	2.4	25.3	22.0	4.7
1937	305.0r	152.0	242	2.5	33.8	25.0	4.7
1938	327.0e	160.0	255	3.5	40.7	26.5e	4.6
1939	358.0r	198.0r	276	4.0	49.3	28.4	4.5
1940	369.0e	200.0	280	5.0	54.0e	30.0e	4.5
1941	441.0r	234.0	336	6.1	69.1	31.4	4.5

e = Estimated   r = Revised datum

[1] Fiscal year ending in year indicated

[2] Vannevar Bush: *Science, the Endless Frontier*; National Science Foundation, Washington, D.C., July 1945 (reprinted July 1960). Yale Brozen: Trends in Industrial Research & Development, *Journal of Business of the University of Chicago*, July 1960

gram that is sure to be reported at the annual stockholders' meeting.

With this acceptance—almost worship—of research, it is not

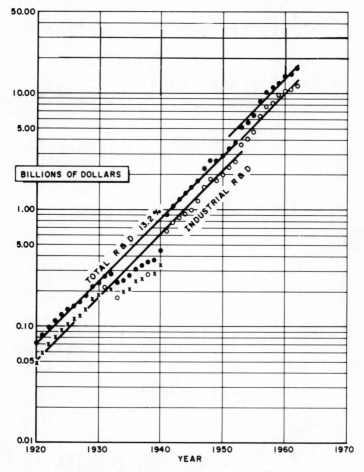

Fig. 1:1 EXPENDITURES FOR RESEARCH AND DEVELOPMENT
(U.S. Totals)

surprising to find that it has grown rapidly. By 1963, total research and development expenditures in the United States had reached 16.4 billion dollars (see Table 1:1). This includes re-

TABLE 1:2

EXPENDITURES FOR RESEARCH AND DEVELOPMENT

(millions of dollars)

Year[1]	Total	Sources of Funds				Use of Funds by			
		Govern-ment	Industry	Colleges and Univer.	Other Nonprofit Instit.	Govern-ment	Industry	Colleges and Univer.	Other Nonprofit Instit.
1942	900	370	510	20	–	200	660	40	–
1943	1,070	490	560	20	–	240	780	50	–
1944	1,210	780	410	20	–	300	850	60	–
1945	1,380	940	420	20	–	390	910	80	–
1946	1,520	1,070	430	20	–	430	990	100	–
1947	1,780	910	840	30	–	470	1,190	120	–
1948	2,260	1,160	1,050	50	–	520	1,570	170	–
1949	2,610	1,390	1,150	70	–	570	1,820	220	–
1950	2,610	1,550	990	70	–	550	1,790	270	–
1951	2,870	1,610	1,180	80	–	570	1,980	320	–
1952	3,360	1,980	1,300	80	–	700	2,300	360	–
1953	3,750	2,240	1,430	80	–	800	2,530	420	–
1954	5,150	2,740	2,240	130	40	970	3,630	450	100
1955	5,620	3,070	2,365	140	45	950	4,070	480	120
1956	6,390	3,670	2,510	155	55	1,090	4,640	530	130
1957	8,670	5,095	3,265	180	70	1,280	6,600	650	140
1958	10,100	6,380	3,390	190	70	1,440	7,730	780	150
1959	11,130	7,170	3,620	190	90	1,730	8,360	840	200
1960	12,680	8,320	4,060	200	100	1,830	9,610	1,000	240
1961	13,890	9,010	4,550	210	120	1,900	10,510	1,200	280
1962 p	14,740	9,650	4,705	230	155	2,090	10,870	1,400	380
1963 p	16,400	11,000	5,000			2,700	11,600		

p = preliminary

[1] Fiscal year ending in year indicated

Source: *Statistical Abstract of the United States:* 1953, 1958, 1962, and 1964 editions.

TABLE 1:2 (Continued)

EXPENDITURES FOR RESEARCH AND DEVELOPMENT

(millions of dollars)

Calendar Year

Cal. Year	Total	Sources of Funds				Use of Funds by			
		Government	Industry	Colleges and Univer.	Other Nonprofit Instit.	Government	Industry	Colleges and Univer.	Other Nonprofit Instit.
1953	5,160	2,760	2,240	120	40	1,010	3,630	420	100
1954	5,660	3,120	2,365	130	45	1,020	4,070	450	120
1955	6,200	3,500	2,510	140	50	950	4,640	480	130
1956	8,370	4,820	3,330	155	65	1,090	6,610	530	140
1957	9,810	6,105	3,455	180	70	1,280	7,730	650	150
1958	10,810	6,840	3,700	190	80	1,440	8,390	780	200
1959	12,430	8,070	4,070	190	100	1,730	9,620	840	240
1960	13,620	8,770	4,540	200	110	1,830	10,510	1,000	280
1961	14,380	9,220	4,810	210	140	1,890	10,910	1,200	380
1962	15,610	10,045	5,175	230	160	2,220	11,540	1,400	350
1963	17,350	11,340	5,565	260	185	2,400	12,720	1,700	530

Source: *Reviews of Data on Science Resources*, Vol. I, No. 4, May 1965; National Science Foundation, Washington, D.C.

search done by industry, by profit and nonprofit research institutes, and by federal and state governments.

The total expenditures for R & D in the United States for the past forty years are shown in Table 1:1 and Figure 1:1. A trend-curve through the data shows a rate of growth around 13.2% a year. The second curve in Figure 1:1 shows the expenditures for R & D by U.S. industry. The relationship of this curve to the total indicates that an essentially constant portion of the R & D has been done in industrial laboratories. In recent years, however, a sizable portion of the R & D by the aircraft, electronics, and some other industries has been financed by government through research contracts and not out of corporate earnings.

Figure 1:2 shows R & D by source of funds. Here the divergence between the industrial R & D and the total is evident. The drop in expenditures for R & D during the early 1930s came primarily in the industrial sector. Research funds from universities and government appear to have remained essentially on a plateau. It is probable, however, that effort in R & D did not decrease in direct proportion to the reduction in dollars that were reported as spent, because of the reductions in wages and salaries during the period.

The data indicate a surge ahead in R & D at the beginning of World War II. Suddenly there was the need to be self-sufficient in products like rubber, and the need for rapid improvement in military aviation and equipment. This wartime impetus carried expenditures up to a level in line with the growth trend of the 1920s. This trend has continued. Recently, the National Science Foundation published revised data back through 1953. For these most recent figures the coverage has been extended so that expenditures appear to show a 60% increase over data previously reported. A trend-line through the data for the eight years for which revised coverage is available, however, shows the same rate of growth as the long-term trend.

The data on expenditures for research and development are expressed in current dollars and so overstate the growth in research effort to the extent of the inflationary increase in wage rates. That this might be sizable is indicated by a fivefold increase in the average annual cost per researcher from 1920 to

1960 (1920 = $2,800; 1960 = $14,000).[1] We know that during
the 1950's wage rates increased about 6% a year, which is about

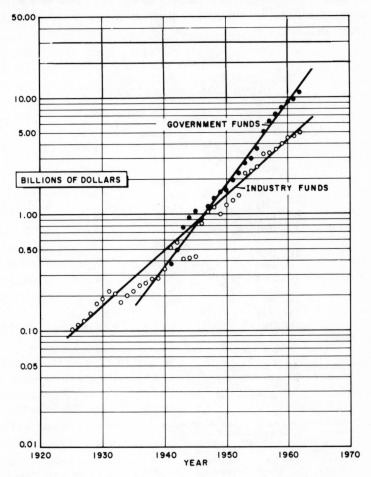

Fig. 1:2 SOURCES FOR FUNDS FOR RESEARCH AND DEVELOPMENT
(U.S. Totals)

twice as fast as average gains in productivity. Since 1960, wage
increases have more nearly matched gains in productivity.

To remove the effects of inflation, the expenditures in re-

[1] Unpublished report.

search dollars should be corrected for the inflationary change in the dollar. This might be done by using the Consumer Price Index, or a suitable commodity price index, or some index of change in labor rates.

TABLE 1:3

RESEARCH PERSONNEL IN
INDUSTRIAL LABORATORIES*

Year	No. Professional Personnel	
1940	–	37,000
1941	62,000[a]	–
1946	80,000	56,000[b]
1947	84,000	–
1948	90,000	–
1949	94,000	–
1950	100,000	70,577[b]
Jan. 1951	–	77,500[b]
1951	104,000	–
Jan. 1952	118,000	95,694[c]
1953	130,000	–
Jan. 1954	–	157,300[d]
1956	–	–
Jan. 1957	–	222,800[e]
Jan. 1959	–	277,000[f]
Jan. 1961	–	307,300[g]

[a] A. L. Lyman, Estimated Volume of Research and Development Expenditures by Industry in 1955, in *Papers of the Fourth Conference on Scientific Manpower;* National Science Foundation, Washington, D.C.: 1954.

[b] *Research and Development Personnel in Industrial Laboratories, 1950,* p. 11; Government Printing Office, Washington, D.C., 1952. 1950 figure is for first half of year.

[c] Bureau of Labor Statistics and Department of Defense, *Scientific Research and Development in American Industry,* pp. 59, 68, 82, 88. Government Printing Office, Washington, D.C., 1953. Nonprofit agencies excluded from this figure.

[d] National Science Foundation, *Science and Engineering in American Industry,* pp. 68, 78. Government Printing Office, Washington, D.C., 1956.

[e] National Science Foundation, *Science and Engineering in American Industry,* p. 62. Government Printing Office, Washington, D.C., 1956.

[f] National Science Foundation, *Foundation Releases Estimates on Employment of Scientists and Engineers in American Industry,* January 1, 1960.

[g] National Science Foundation, *Research and Development in Industry,* 1960.

* Source (thru January 1959): Excerpt from Yale Brozen's article: Trends in industrial research and development; Reprinted from *The Journal of Business of the University of Chicago,* Vol. 33, No. 3, July 1960.

Another method of removing the inflationary distortions caused by the loss of purchasing power of the dollar would be to use the record on the growth in the number of research workers. Table 1:3 and Figure 1:3 show the number of employees engaged in research in industrial laboratories. The average rate of growth of professional employees in industrial laboratories is almost 9.5% a year. By contrast, total employees

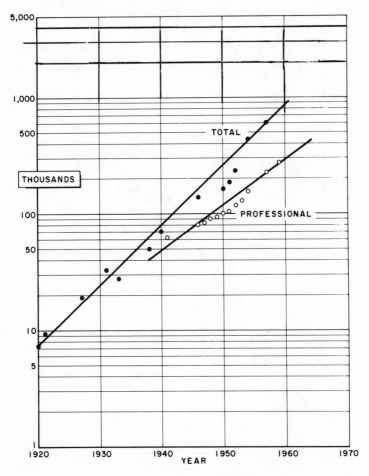

Fig. 1:3 Research Personnel in Industrial Laboratories

in industrial research have been increasing at about 12.5% a year. This indicates an increasing rise of nontechnical employees as assistants to improve efficiency. On the average, industry is now using about 1.5 assistants for each technically

trained researcher. Figures 1:4 and 1:5 show data on membership in the American Chemical Society and the American Institute of Chemical Engineers.

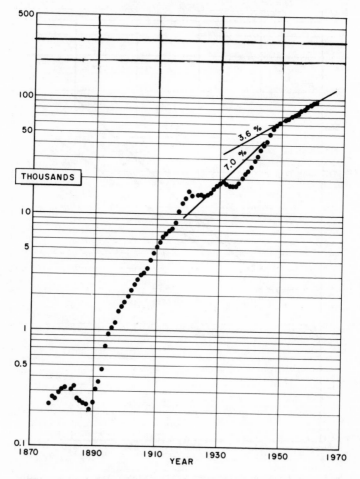

Fig. 1:4 MEMBERSHIP OF AMERICAN CHEMICAL SOCIETY

It should be noted that both this method and deflated expenditures for research tend to understate the research done,
because they take no account of increase in productivity. The

true picture will lie somewhere between that indicated by the actual and the deflated expenditures for research.

There is an additional factor which further exaggerates the

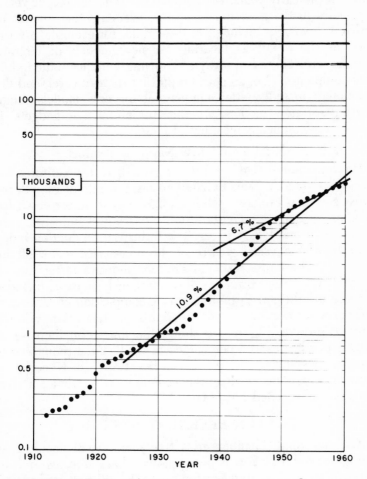

Fig. 1:5 MEMBERSHIP OF AMERICAN INSTITUTE OF CHEMICAL ENGINEERS

data on the indicated increase in industrial expenditures. In the early part of this century, there were few well-defined industrial research laboratories. In many companies, especially

the smaller ones, research-and-development was done in production units and was not budgeted separately as research. In
all probability, the figures for dollars understate the research
effort in the early years. By contrast, the data for recent years,
especially in the government sector, overstate the amount of
research involved. Included in these data, for example, are the
cost for the detail engineering for new models of aircraft,
missiles, etc. There is no way of knowing whether some industrial companies, also, do not in reporting their research and development include detail engineering for new models. Engineering for new models, whether for aircraft or gadgets, is
hardly *research* in any meaningful sense.

R & D Exceeds 2.5% of Gross National Product

We have noted that the rate of growth in expenditures for
research is 13.2% a year. By comparison, the rate of growth for
Gross National Product (GNP) is 5.5% a year, uncorrected for
inflation, or 2.8% on a constant dollar basis; and Industrial Production is, at most, 3.5% a year. The Industrial Production Index
indicates the physical growth of the nonservice sector of the
economy. The Gross National Product shows a faster rate of
growth even after correction for inflation, because it includes
services in addition to production. A comparison of GNP and
R&D expenditures on a current dollar basis shows their relative
rates of growth. Figure 1:6 shows the long-term increase in
R&D expenditures as a percentage of GNP. Even though costs
may be overstated relative to earlier times, it is certainly
growing much faster than the economy as a whole, and it
has already exceeded 2.5% of G N P.

NEED FOR EFFICIENT RESEARCH

At some point, members of a free society will decide that
enough of today's effort is being plowed back into research to
improve tomorrow. Budgets for research will not expand beyond this point.[2] If we wish to accelerate our rate of progress,
we will have to get a breakthrough in efforts to increase efficiency in research.

---

[2] Yale Brozen predicts an upper limit of research expenditures of 5.2% of GNP
by 1973; *The Journal of Business of the University of Chicago,* July 1960.

From the size of the national research budget and its relation to national income, it is evident that it would be desirable to increase efficiency in research. The question is, *HOW?* What

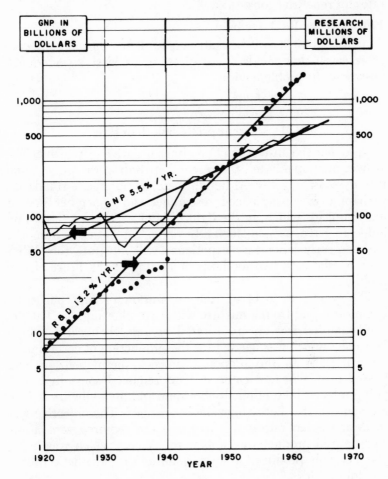

Fig. 1:6 RESEARCH EXPENDITURES AND GROSS NATIONAL PRODUCT

does efficiency in research mean? This in itself poses something of a problem. If the answer to a problem is unknown, how can one judge what is a quick solution and what is a slow one; or even how to differentiate between a good solution and a poor one? One cannot even foreknow the chances for success with a project in a given field. There are no quantitative standards that can be set in the way that time-study can standardize the rates for repetitive jobs.

Efficiency in R&D Defined

At this point it will be sufficient to define *efficient research* as research that yields a complete, or at least an adequate, answer to the problem with:

1. A minimum of effort,
2. A low expense,
3. In an appropriate length of time.

Note that the answer may be either negative or positive. The answer may merely tell the researcher to drop the project and turn to something else. Although there are no precise standards, perhaps every experienced researcher can remember one or more projects which, in the light of later experience, he would judge to have been inefficiently done. An example from the author's early laboratory experience will illustrate the difference by showing two methods of getting at the heart of one problem.

The problem[3] involved the separation of one particular chemical liquid from a mixture with two other liquids. The desired material was an unsaturated organic chemical (divinylbenzene) which was needed for the production of certain plastic materials. In the proposed process, diethylbenzene was passed over a heated catalyst. This removed some hydrogen and produced both ethylvinylbenzene and divinylbenzene, and left some of the diethylbenzene unchanged. The objective was to design a laboratory still to make the required separation. The desired product was similar to styrene, which was being commercially produced in large quantities for synthetic rubber and for plastics.

Months were consumed in trying to develop a more effective laboratory still—one with more theoretical plates. This seemed a natural step because the process appeared to be similar to the separation used in the production of styrene. One day I

---

[3] For details, see end of chapter.

decided to analyze the problem by making some preliminary chemical engineering calculations concerning the still that would be required. At this point some of the necessary data were missing, so approximate boiling points were obtained from batch distillation curves, and the vapor pressure at different temperatures for each of the three chemicals was estimated.

To my great surprise, these preliminary calculations showed that only about a dozen "theoretical plates" were required—not the hundred or more that had been assumed necessary by analogy with the process for styrene.

These preliminary calculations brought to light the fact that it was not necessary to separate the third component—the high boiling liquid—in pure form. It would be sufficient to obtain a product consisting of the high-boiling liquid and part of the intermediate-boiling liquid, and leave the rest of the inter-mediate liquid and the original material as a residue.

As a matter of hindsight, it was easy to see that a more care-ful analysis of the problem would have indicated this difference at the beginning of the project; or that the calculations with the crude data should have been made sooner, as the approximate data were available early in the work. Here, surely, is a case where much time and effort were wasted as a result of the way the research was done. This realization started my interest in the question of how to attack a research problem.

Instruction Speeds Learning

Some may say, "Well, skill in attacking a research problem is the difference between an experienced and an inexperienced man." If that is so, then there is something that the experienced researcher has learned by trial and error. Perhaps with some help and guidance the young scientist could mature more quickly.

WHEN THERE IS SOMETHING TO BE LEARNED, GOOD
INSTRUCTION CAN SHORTEN THE LEARNING PERIOD

How can the young scientist be given help in developing judgment and skill in analyzing and solving problems? HOW? That is the most difficult type of question, more difficult than a WHAT question. The libraries are full of books on *what* to do, but outside the manual arts one finds few hints on *how* to do what one *ought* to do. It is hard enough to do a good job of instruction on a manual operation. It is much more difficult to develop techniques for jobs that involve primarily the use of mental tools; nevertheless, that is the objective before us. In the succeeding chapters are set forth concrete suggestions on some important ways to improve efficiency in research; and although some are rather general, nevertheless every effort has been made to offer specific suggestions, rather than broad generalities.

Research Is Mental

To think of research as essentially a mental process may be surprising to many, after the stress laid on laboratory work in the teaching of science in our schools and colleges. Laboratory work is the lesser important step in research. *Creative thinking,* the conceiving of a new idea, is the essence of research. As Harold DeForest Arnold[4] has stated:

Research is of the mind, not of the hands, a concentration of thought and not a process of experimentation. Research is the effort of the mind to comprehend relationships which no one had previously known.

Or, as Charles F. Kettering[5] has stated:

What an inventor or research engineer tries to do is to discover the factors in a problem by experimental evaluation. This is quite different from the cut-and-try method, since it emphasizes evaluation as much as it does experimentation.

He is also credited with saying:

A problem is not solved in the laboratory. It is solved in some fellow's head. He only needs the laboratory apparatus to get his head turned around so he can see the thing right.

This emphasis on the mental processes is not intended to imply scorn of laboratory work. But mere *experimentation* has become so synonymous with *research* that there is need to remind ourselves that the idea—the thinking step—usually comes first and the experiment then follows as a testing of the idea. To be sure, the laboratory work is an inseparable companion

---

[4] From a lecture given at Lowell Institute by Harold DeForest Arnold shortly before his death.
[5] *The Rotarian,* January 1952.

to creative thinking, and efficient methods in both are required if the total effort is to be effective. The greatest savings, however, can be in a discriminating selection of the problem, the organization of the work, and the method of attacking the problem—the mental part.

Once my attention had been fixed on the problem of efficiency, it was evident that meandering, halting research seemed to be a common experience. Inquiry confirms the suspicion that universities pay little attention to the question of *how* to do research. Whatever the student, even at the graduate level, learns about how to attack a problem, he usually learns by unconscious imitation of the professors, and by trial and error. It is evident that much could be done to help the young researcher to develop skill and maturity in this important task.

An examination of the literature gives no ready-made answer to the problem of efficient research. Examination and reexamination of my own procedures helped me, but more profitable was the questioning of older research leaders on how one should go about attacking a problem in research. From my senior colleagues came suggestions—some good, some indifferent, and some direct contradictions. These ideas were studied, using classical definitions of the SCIENTIFIC METHOD as a frame of reference, and it became clear that there were some missing links. After much study of the *problem of solving problems* the missing links were discovered, and the factors were finally integrated into the method that is the main thesis of the first part of this book. Thus, many of the ideas that are set forth here are, in reality, the considered views of more than a score of successful research men in industrial and academic laboratories.

Finally, the method as set forth in this book has been tested with younger research men. Several groups of ten or twelve research workers were brought together in conference to study the method. They then applied the method of attacking a problem to problems brought in by members of the group. The results were highly gratifying.

At this stage perhaps one may ask, "How important is efficiency in research? Is there much to be gained by increasing this efficiency?" The limits of possible gain can be learned by comparing the results of the most prolific against those of the least effective researcher. Obviously, nothing is going to develop the dullard into a genius. If, however, the inefficient could be upgraded to average and the average to superior, much increase in productivity would result, and this increase in efficiency in research would benefit all groups in society.

On a national scale, getting more and better results from the researchers now in the laboratories would, in part, mitigate the shortage of trained scientists. In the long-term struggle between this nation and any other nation, our ability to survive will depend largely on our staying ahead in technology. If any enemy nation or nations train more scientists than we do, then we must train ours to be more efficient than theirs.

R&D Escalates Progress

More efficient research will help us to retain our technological advantage and at the same time further raise our standard of living. The whole object of research is to find new and simpler means to predict and control our environment. The result of scientific activities is an increase in our ability to supply human wants with less total effort. The cost of goods and services is little more than the sum of the costs of all labor that goes into the given article. These costs include the wages for mining the raw materials; the wages of all that handle, process, fabricate, and transport at various stages of production, or store the product until purchased. They include also interest, the wages of capital, and finally profits, entrepreneurial wages. Hence, if scientists and engineers can find processes that require less labor, or products that last longer, the consumer receives more for his money. With the leftover money he can purchase something else that he wants, thus enjoying a higher standard of living.

The employer will also reap a direct benefit if the research workers show greater efficiency. Not only will he get more for his research dollar, but what is even more important, quick solutions to problems will help him stay ahead of his competitors in the battle for markets. If the research group develops new and better processes and products quickly, the company can get into the market with the new product first, and can expand and grow more rapidly. Now it just happens that in an expanding company there are more and better jobs for all employees, including the research men. On the other hand, the company that is losing its markets is likely to retract, rather than expand, research.

Yes, more efficient research means a better job for the researcher. If he earns a reputation for obtaining clean-cut answers quickly, he finds sources of increased satisfaction. In the first place, he enjoys his work more. Few things are more stimulating than finding a good solution to a hard problem. Secondly, the efficient research worker will be accorded more recognition from his associates; and who does not like to be esteemed by his fellow men? Thirdly, the ability to produce clean-cut results quickly, leads to faster advancement. No man can expect to be entrusted with leadership of others until he has demonstrated that he can direct his own efforts successfully.

In short, increased efficiency in research will obtain for the individual:

1. More personal satisfaction
2. More pay

Is that important to you? Is it important to the men working under your supervision?

Research has grown to its present importance because of its great contribution to society. New ideas, inventions, and better techniques are the stepping-stones by which society climbs to the more abundant life. Experimentation is the means by which we bring about constructive change that leads to greater efficiency. Research is the systematic approach to experimentation and it has become recognized as the very basis of progress. For this reason increased efficiency in doing research offers great rewards. As we shall see in Chapter 6, the leverage of a new idea may be as much as several hundredfold. Consequently, even a small improvement in efficiency in research shows promise of being multiplied manyfold.

Management can borrow from the technique of the researcher, himself, who when he has a tough problem *analyzes it, breaks it apart,* and attacks it piecemeal. He tries to discover the forces involved, the degrees of freedom in the system, and then he studies these factors one by one. This type of procedure shows promise with the problem at hand.

Analysis of the problem indicates at least nine major factors that significantly influence efficiency in research.

Researcher's Responsibility

Chapters 2, 3, 4, and 5 will examine three factors that lie primarily in the province of the researcher's own initiative. These three factors are:

1. The method of attacking the problem;
2. The reporting of the results of research; and
3. The training of the researcher.

Management may motivate the researcher to continue his studies. Management may set standards and encourage the researcher to do a good job of reporting. It may also conduct seminars or by other means attempt to assist researchers in improving their research techniques. Basically, however, in these three areas anything that management may do is only indirect. The prime responsibility and initiative must lie with the researcher, himself.

Management's Responsibility

Organized effort by a group always calls for leadership. In the business world we call this leadership *management*, and it is to the managers of research that business entrusts the quest for more effective research. In organizing and directing the efforts of researchers, there are six factors for which management is primarily responsible. To be sure, the individual researcher is not passive on many of these factors and he can make a positive contribution. Nevertheless, management must supply the leadership and establish an environment conducive to efficient research. The six factors that are the primary responsibility of management are:

1. Selection of the problem
2. Selection and assignment of the researcher
3. Organization of the research
4. Equipment
5. Morale
6. Communications

In subsequent chapters, each of these nine factors will be

examined to see what procedures and techniques show promise of improving results. The reader should look not for a formula by which research can be turned over to an electronic brain, but rather, for helpful suggestions from experience and from recent research on problems of organization and morale. When both researchers and management intelligently apply all the art that has been developed in this field, the total result will surely be a considerable increase in productivity in scientific research.

SUPPLEMENTARY NOTES

PREPARATION OF DIVINYLBENZENE

This more detailed description of the problem mentioned on page 16 is included for those that care to note the technical details of the problem. This problem arose in connection with an attempt to get a cross-linked plastic from styrene. The divinylbenzene, with two vinyl groups, will copolymerize with styrene (vinylbenzene) to give a branched and cross-linked, rather than a straight-chain polymer.

In the production of styrene, two hydrogen atoms are removed from ethylbenzene to give styrene (vinylbenzene). The liquid reaction product consists essentially of a mixture of ethylbenzene (the original product, unreacted) and styrene. The two are then separated by distillation, but require stills with about 80 especially designed trays or plates.

In a similar manner, diethylbenzene can be dehydrogenated. In this reaction, however, the product contained some of the original diethylbenzene, some ethylvinylbenzene (only one-half dehydrogenated), and the desired divinylbenzene. Continuing the analogy, distillation seemed a suitable way to separate the desired product, divinylbenzene, from the mixture. As the products and the processes were similar, laboratory stills were set up using the principle of vacuum columns in series, which was successful in commercial styrene plants. Months were consumed in trying to develop continuous laboratory columns with more and more plates, and in trying to isolate pure isomers of each of the materials to get precise physical properties. The work was progressing very slowly. One day I tried some chemical calculations to make a preliminary estimate of the number of plates required.

For the major components of the mixture I obtained boiling points from the plateaus of batch distillation curves and then drew vapor pressure lines on Cox charts; this gave approximate curves for vapor pressure plotted against temperature. From this a McCabe-Thiele diagram for vapor-liquid equilibrium was constructed, and the number of theoretical plates required for the desired separation was estimated graphically. The results were so surprising that a more refined analysis—a "plate-to-plate count"—was made. It verified the conclusions that only a dozen or so theoretical plates would be required to make the separation.

By analogy with styrene, I had expected this separation to require 80 to 100 theoretical plates instead of a mere dozen. How did this separation differ from the purification of styrene? Why had I wasted months trying to get pure divinylbenzene? The separation of styrene involved basically a two-component system—styrene and ethylbenzene. To produce plastics or synthetic rubber it is necessary to separate the styrene to about 99% purity or better. The divinyl system, on the other hand, was for all practical purposes a three-component system—divinylbenzene, ethylvinylbenzene, and diethylbenzene. Divinylbenzene was used by mixing it with styrene (vinylbenzene) to give cross-linking during polymerization, thereby yielding a polymer that would not soften and flow at elevated temperatures. It was known that ethylvinylbenzene (a homologue of styrene) could be substituted for part of the styrene without changing the results. Hence, in this separation it was not necessary to obtain pure divinylbenzene; it was necessary only to remove all the diethylbenzene. For this reason the intermediate ethylvinylbenzene fraction could be split, part being taken overhead with the divinylbenzene, and part taken off at the bottom of the column with the diethylbenzene, thus making a relatively easy separation.

chapter 2

A METHOD OF
SOLVING PROBLEMS

There are many ways to attack a problem in scientific research, but they are not all equally effective. What is needed is a method that will give uniformly good results on all problems. This does not mean that a solution will be found for all problems, but it does mean that the researcher will have so attacked the problem that he did not overlook obvious points or do any unnecessary experiments. It does mean that the project will be carried forward systematically to a positive or negative answer, with a minimum of effort, expense, and time.

In Chapter 1 the solution to a problem involving distillation was outlined. The solution to that problem gives a clue to a good method of attacking another similar problem. The trouble is that before that particular problem comes up again there will be a great many other problems with no apparent similarity. Can some principles be developed that will apply to all problems?

The Scientific Method

"Use the scientific method" is the answer most frequently given by experienced research workers. This is not a surprising answer for scientists, even though many trained in the physical sciences cannot state the scientific method. What, then, is the scientific method? It has been stated in many ways; the simplest is:

1. Assemble the facts;
2. Correlate the facts;
3. Draw valid conclusions.

No fewer than these three steps can be considered the scientific method, although a fourth step is usually added; namely, test the conclusions with additional experiments.

In the 17th century, Robert Boyle proposed the following steps:

1. Assemble the facts;
2. Construct a hypothesis relating the facts;
3. Test the hypothesis with new experiments;
4. If these disprove the hypothesis, construct a new one using the old and the new facts;
5. Repeat until a solution is obtained.

This method certainly is general enough and valid; it ought to produce results. But is not such a statement a little *too general* to be of much help?

These suggestions are something like telling a young musician that the way to compose a song hit is to select and place notes one after the other in such a manner that they make a song with a pleasant melody and good rhythm. The real problem is, HOW? What notes does he select and in what order does he place them?

Precisely what the inexperienced research worker needs is some clues and hints on how to assemble the facts; how best to correlate the facts; and how to draw valid conclusions or construct the hypothesis. When the scientific method is fully stated, it is found to embody six steps:

1. State the *objective;*
2. Assemble the *facts;*
3. *Organize* the facts;
4. Propose likely *solution;*
5. *Test* the solution;
6. *Sell* results—take action (see Chapter 4)

The scientific method puts much emphasis on getting the facts. But in attacking a problem there is a prior step before assembling the facts. First the objective must be determined. So important is this step that the solution sometimes becomes evident when the problem is properly stated. Some go so far as to say that problem-solving consists in finding a proper statement of the problem.

I. State the Objective

Research problems present themselves in many ways. They may be assigned by management; they may be the researcher's own brain child; or they may just grow, "like Topsy". In any case, the research worker should arrive at a definite objective as the first step in attacking his problem. If he is part of a research organization, he should make it *his responsibility* to ask questions and talk over the objective with his supervisor.

Many a junior researcher may feel that this is the supervisor's responsibility—that the research director should tell him what is to be done. Such an attitude is apt to lead to poor results. In the first place, a research leader is frequently a very busy man. He may, unless questioned, take time for only a preliminary statement of the problem. Anyway, the research man, and he alone, knows the boundaries of his knowledge concerning the particular problem. In the ideal case, both the supervisor and the researcher assume responsibility for a clear, adequate statement of the objective, for this, obviously, would lead to the best results. Sometimes the skillful supervisor can help the researcher to set up intermediate objectives which collectively and progressively lead to the major objective.

State Objective Positively

In stating the objective, always *state it positively*, but never formulate it in such a way as to indicate that the aim is to prove something. If the objective is to prove some hypothesis, this objective cannot be obtained if the hypothesis is wrong. For example, how good a plastic is compound X; not, prove that plastic X is better than plastic Y. Solution of this problem may involve comparing X with Y, but now the objective can be attained no matter which is better. The research type of problem-solving should not be confused with exercises in mathematical logic; hence, scrupulously avoid the "to prove" type of phrase in stating the objective for a research problem.

State Over-all and Immediate Objectives

In stating the objective it is generally advisable to state both an *over-all objective* and an *immediate objective*. The over-all objective is something more general than the immediate one. It is the kind of concept that is fathered by the thought, "What could I contribute to other important problems by looking at this one a little more broadly?" The over-all objective will encourage the researcher to obtain at least a few points of data in the uncommon regions—data that sometimes show surprising results.

For example, a problem might come to a researcher stated something like this: Improve a finishing still in a process plant so that it will deliver a product of higher purity. The over-all objective is a production of the desired purity. As stated, however, the problem assumes that the operation of the finishing still must be improved. If during the course of the investigation it develops that the major trouble lies in operations that precede the finishing still, then an adequate solution of the problem so stated could not be found. As a first step, then, the problem should be restated. The over-all objective would be higher purity and the immediate objective would be improved operation of the finishing still. Such a statement of the problem invites broader consideration.

Past experience teaches that really new and significant advances are most often made by attacking a problem well back at its roots. This sort of approach is encouraged by carefully stating an over-all objective for the problem under consideration, sometimes very broadly. The important advances are made by applying a comprehensive point of view; see Chapter 6.

Additional examples may help to clarify the nature of the over-all objective. In a study of antibiotics, the real objective would not be a new and cheap method to make penicillin, but rather a cheap, nontoxic agent to kill bacteria in the human body. The best solution may or may not be penicillin. The major objective in still another area is not a new cracking technique to make higher-octane gasoline for high-compression engines, but rather a new fuel-engine combination which gets better performance per unit of fuel. This may involve changes in the fuel, in the engine, or in both. The objective should be a more satisfactory container, not merely an improved closure.

Reexamine Objective

The objective should be reexamined after each of the subsequent steps in attacking the problem. New facts may give better insight and permit a better statement of the objective. It may be possible to narrow the objective, or the analysis in step 3 may require a broadening of the objective.

If the research worker is a university professor doing pioneer research under his own direction and initiative, he too will want to carefully state his objective, but motivation will be no problem. In a research group, on the other hand, the director and group leaders will probably have to do some motivating if good results are to be obtained. As the question of motivation will be discussed in Chapter 7, it will be sufficient here to note that part of rousing the researcher's interest consists in telling the reasons why. This can be made a part of stating the objective, especially the over-all objective.

II. Assemble the Facts

The second step is to get the facts. What facts? How many facts? The answer is simple to state but hard to define. Get *all available, pertinent facts!* How does one know when one has all the facts that are available? What facts are pertinent to the particular problem? And how can one recognize a *fact,* i.e., what is fact and what is half-truth?

Should one first go to the library? If so, should he seek out the latest journals so as to learn the most recent facts, or a book on the subject? What about questioning one's colleagues? Or, is it best to go directly into the laboratory to run some experiments to get the desired facts? In the majority of cases, most or all of these methods should be used. The important thing is the order in which these are used and the proper balance between them, depending on the particular problem and the individual's acquaintance in the field.

The consensus among experienced researchers is that *first* one should turn to his own experience for facts pertinent to the problem, assuming of course that the field is not completely new to the researcher. In this preliminary stage, he would do well to jump ahead and break the problem down as outlined in step 3, and then suggest solutions, as indicated in step 4. By spending some time in considering the problem before seeking the experience of others, the researcher brings his own experience and ingenuity to bear on the problem before there can be any chance of becoming prejudiced by the results or methods of others. It is recommended that one actually write down his own ideas about the problem at this point. Writing them ensures more careful consideration than is likely otherwise.

The next step depends largely on how well the individual is acquainted with the particular field. If he is generally familiar with the field and is part of a research organization, the next logical step should be to confer with colleagues who have some experience in the field. If the field is rather new to the researcher, he may have to start at the beginning by consulting a good reference book on the subject and then studying the journals for more recent facts.

The whole objective of seeking out the experience of others at this stage is to make use of the accumulative knowledge in the field. The great strides that the sciences have made would not have been possible if each scientist had started from the beginning each time he had a problem and had learned nothing from his predecessors. In the interest of efficiency, each of us should learn as much as we can from the experience of others.

In using the experience of others, however, always be a "doubting Thomas." The research man must assume the critical attitude regarding all literature and even suggestions from colleagues. It is hard to overcome the tendency to accept the printed word, especially those in well-bound books, as having a special validity, even finality. Guard against this tendency. The researcher must constantly remind himself that what is recorded in the literature frequently does not represent complete facts, but rather only "half truths." Especially must one be careful about accepting conclusions as stated in the literature, or even the drawing of conclusions from data in the literature. Critically study the information reported by an author, including his procedures and assumptions, stated or implied. Be especially skeptical of negative results. Avoid making conclusions at this point. Collect information impartially.

During the fact-getting stage one should pay attention to

analogies and partial solutions to the problem. These are very tricky, however, as they have a special fascination and are apt to lead one's thinking into a bypath. Figure 2:1 shows how easily one's conclusions can be prejudiced by experience.

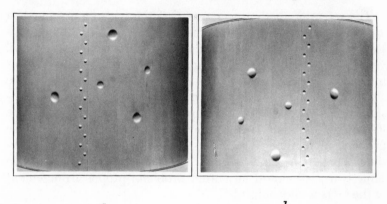

a   *b*

Fig. 2:1 TANK SHOWING INDENTATIONS AND PROTRUSIONS
b is the same photograph as *a*, but inverted

Notice which tank has dents and which has bumps. Now turn the page upside down and note how the bumps become dents, and vice versa. In reality, these are two copies of the same picture, one being inverted. The impression given here results from the fact that we are accustomed to seeing objects lighted from the top, so a shadow at the top indicates an indentation. This pair of pictures indicates how unconscious and automatic is the influence of preconditioning. Truly, one must exert a real effort to offset it in himself. Remember that every author's report has been influenced by his prejudices and preconditioning. Someone else might have made different observations or recorded additional data, which in turn would lead to different conclusions.

In assembling the facts, it is sometimes wise to go into the laboratory and run some preliminary, test-tube-type experiments. Sometimes a few exploratory tests will do much to acquaint the researcher with the nature of the problem. These should not be extensive or elaborate experiments at this stage;

it is more a matter of acquiring firsthand impressions about the problem.

III. Organize the Facts

The scientific method suggests that the facts be arranged in an orderly fashion. Of all the aspects of problem-solving, this step is generally done more haphazardly than any other, and yet this is probably the most important single step for obtaining uniformly good results in solving problems. One can have a notion of the importance of properly arranging facts by considering how useless the data in a railroad timetable would be if it were recorded in a haphazard arrangement. The simple problem of mapping a railroad journey is much simplified by the particular organization of the facts in the timetable. The same is true of almost any other problem; proper arrangement of the facts is very helpful.

Some writers in discussing the scientific method say that in drawing valid conclusion from the facts, one should apply superior judgment. That sounds good, but what is "superior judgment," and where is it to be found? By this term the authors mean that one should bring all his *pertinent past experience* to bear on the given problem. The breakdown of the problem, as indicated here, is especially designed to help the researcher bring to the problem all his most pertinent experience.

Writing down the answers to the steps as outlined will focus attention on the heart of the problem and help to avoid bypaths that do not lead toward the objective. It can also assist in deciding just what additional facts are needed to permit logical solutions to be considered.

Will this not prevent serendipity—those chance discoveries which often are more important than the solution of the original problem? This is not likely. Actually, logical thorough consideration of the current problem should *assist* in noting any significant side or unexpected results. Any unusual result would have a better chance of being noticed and evaluated, because it would not fit into the analysis of the problem and would be recognized as unusual.

List of Steps

Many problems can be broken down into two or more separate problems or major steps. Solving each step in turn gives a complete solution to the problem.

But what if there are two or more alternative routes? And suppose several of the alternative methods are coupled in series?

Usually any extensive problem can be broken down into a series of parallel and series problems offering a variety of paths to reach a final solution. The different possibilities might be symbolized as shown in Figure 2:2.

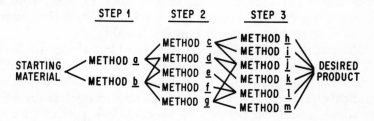

Fig. 2:2 Typical Procedure in Solving a Problem

If several steps are involved with more than one possibility in each step, the total of possible combinations becomes large. To increase the difficulty, each choice in one step may automatically eliminate certain choices in subsequent steps.

On a new problem, the researcher should map out all alternatives known to him before selecting any particular route on which to concentrate. In listing the individual steps of the problem, consider the criteria listed next. The factors involved in the selection of the particular route are much like those involved in the selection of the original problem itself. This will be discussed at length in Chapter 6.

Orderly Arrangement of Information

The following information should be listed for each step. *Listing* here means actually writing down, if the problem is at all involved. Writing these points down assures more careful consideration of the problem and sifts out the pertinent experience to be applied against the problem.

1) *Scientific Field Involved:*

After selecting the natural steps in the problem, next select the field of science to which the specific problem for each step belongs. The term *field of science* as used here is not meant to differentiate between the sciences of chemistry and physics or zoology, etc., nor even such major divisions of science as physical, organic, inorganic, and analytical chemistry. The field of science here refers rather to a smaller subdivision, just that portion covered by a given set of closely related natural laws. The researcher should be thinking of such classifications as kinetics, reaction equilibrium, phase relations, fluid flow, automatic control, magnetism, electronics, heredity, etc.

For each such field of science the present knowledge has been developed into more or less well-defined concepts and theories which are frequently reduced to definite rules or even to mathematical equations. When a trained scientist recognizes the field to which a problem belongs, he knows which part of his and other scientists' experiences should be brought to bear on the problem. For example, most problems involving chemical separations belong in the field of phase relations, and the experienced researcher seeks solutions for this type problem by use of data on phase relations. Determining the scientific field aids in selecting the known variables, which is the next step.

2) *Known Variables:*

Having determined the field of the problem, it is usually easy to enumerate the known variables. Often, the general nature of the influence of the variables is also known; for example, the relation between a change in temperature and rates of reaction; or the relation between a change in pressure and the shift of an equilibrium if there is a change in volume.

What about unknown variables? There is always the possibility that an important variable is not known. The research man must always keep an open mind on this; he must, in fact, be constantly looking for new variables. The new variable may be the key to the problem.

3) *Type of Data Required:*

Attention should next be directed to the type of data required. Items 1 and 2 above set the stage for this. Knowing the scientific field and the variables involved, it is usually easy to determine the type of data required. For example, in problems involving phase relations, it is obvious that data on phase equilibrium are required.

In organizing the assembled facts, it may be found that some basic data are missing. What is to be done about this? How can the missing data be obtained? Sometimes they must be developed by careful experimentation. Above all, a scientist must avoid developing judgments and conclusions without adequate facts. The key point here, however, is how accurate must the required data be? A little reflection will lead any of us to realize that more often than not, approximate data will suffice for the considerations in this preliminary attack on the problem. Usually, it is sufficient in the first solution of the problem merely to learn whether or not the hypothesis is true. The question of exact relationships are needed primarily by the engineers when the idea or process is to be exploited.

The problem of purifying divinylbenzene by that distillation, which was discussed in Chapter 1, is a good example. Use of curves for approximate vapor pressure, extrapolated from approximate data on boiling points, were adequate to give preliminary proof of a solution to the problem. This is another example which further illustrates how improvised data led to proper analysis of a problem.

Some years ago I was attempting to prepare some pure m-diethylbenzene in order to measure its physical properties. Careful distillation had yielded about two liters of product of 99.4% purity. At that point a quite natural assumption was made, namely that a couple of recrystallizations would yield material of high purity, so the sample was cooled until half of it had crystallized. The rest of the liquid was decanted.

The process was repeated a second time. To my surprise and disappointment, the purity had been increased to only 99.6%. I then tried to figure out why. The melting point of the m-isomer was known to be about $-84.2°C$, from extrapolation of a measurement on the 99.4% sample. Moreover, the impurity was known to be primarily the *ortho*-isomer. Further, the melting point of the *ortho*-compound was known to be in the region of $-20°$ to $-40°C$. With this information I constructed a phase equilibrium diagram, as shown in Figure 2:3. It is possible to construct such a diagram of approximate equilibrium without additional data because, as a general rule, similar angles are formed between the lines for composition and a horizontal line through the eutectic.

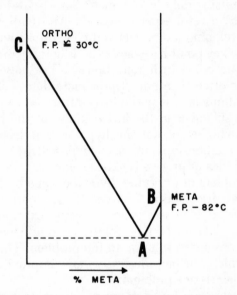

Fig. 2:3 TYPICAL DIAGRAM OF PHASE EQUILIBRIUM

Even a hasty glance at the diagram explained the difficulty. Because the starting material was nearly pure *meta,* as the temperature was lowered the composition changed along line *AB,* and by the time 10 or 15 percent had crystallized, the composition had changed to the eutectic mixture and no further separation occurred.

Two conclusions follow:

    a) I had had enough data to analyze the problem to this conclusion before the attempts to purify further; and *b*) Had I analyzed the problem in this way at first, I would either have discarded the idea of further purification by crystallization, or else I would have frozen out a mere 8 to 10 percent, and undoubtedly some pure product would have been obtained.

In this case, knowledge of the melting point of the impurity to an accuracy of $\pm 10°C$ was adequate. Often, considerable strides can be made in analyzing a problem with relatively crude data.

This is not always true. Sometimes even the best data available are not good enough. When using thermo-data for calculating free energy changes for reactions, slight errors in the data will sometimes reverse the answer.

The story is told that Willard H. Dow used to impress this point on new research chemists by asking them to calculate the feasibility of a certain reaction. When the calculations gave a positive free energy change and the researcher was convinced that the reaction would not go in the desired direction, Dr. Dow would conduct him out to the plant where the reaction was proceeding beautifully on a commercial scale. The trouble was not with the usefulness of thermodynamic calculations. The fault lay in making calculations with thermal data that were not sufficiently accurate.

One must use judgment. As a guidepost or first approximation, assume that the degree of accuracy required is some function of the difference in percentage in the values of any two data being compared. In the freezing diagram shown in Figure 2:3, for instance, the melting points were so widely separated that considerable variation in the value of one of them would not alter the general conclusion. In thermodynamic calculation, on the other hand, the difference between two large numbers may be only a small percent of the absolute value of either. In most cases, for the preliminary testing of a hypothesis, one can tolerate uncertainty of even 10% of the *difference* between the quantities.

4) *Known Methods:*

Listing known methods of attacking the problem, or certain aspects of it, can sometimes help to focus one's pertinent experience on the problem. In a problem involving flow of a viscous liquid through an orifice, we can remind ourselves that flow can be caused by the force of gravity, by mechanical pressure by a piston, by fluid pressure (direct or indirect through vacuum), or by centrifugal force. Problems involving chemical separation may be solved by such processes as distillation, crystallization, absorption, adsorption, ion exchange, thermal diffusion, or chemical reaction.

5) *Opposites:*

Some research workers think that it helps to list opposites, to bring out the contrasts. This way of looking at a problem may be more helpful for some individuals than for others. In any case, if other approaches fail, the consideration of opposites may open up a new train of thought.

6) *Costs:*

There are two aspects of costs to which the research man should give some attention, the amount of attention to each being determined by the objective of the research. The first is the cost of doing the research by different methods, as there may be more difference than is normally supposed. The second is a reevaluation of the project to determine whether it warrants the proposed expenditure for research.

That a project is worthwhile is a key factor in improving productivity of research. This factor is so important that even the research man at the bench must keep it in mind lest he find himself working on a problem that is not worth the effort. The research man must be ready to drop a partially completed project if a change in the situation makes the answer to the problem unimportant. It is hard to do this, but the researcher must sternly curb his natural desire to "see it through," if completing the project has lost its significance.

Sometimes a very convinced and obstinate research man has continued with a project and succeeded when the odds have appeared overwhelmingly against success. If management has lost confidence in the project, progress in research will be more difficult through lack of psychological support and appropriations. Under the best of circumstances, the research man is playing very long odds when he does not have his management with him. If he ever feels inclined to go it alone in the face of all odds, he should be sure that the rewards are worth the risks; that the product or process sought will be really profitable if discovered (see Chapter 6).

Ideally, the cost factors in the problem will have been fully evaluated before it is accepted by supervision as an active project. But it frequently happens that after the second step (assembling facts) a reconsideration of costs will be advisable. The key to these considerations lies in the fact that it is the researcher's responsibility to spend both the money allotted to the project, and his own precious time as intelligently as possible. He should be as cost-conscious as if he were spending his own money.

As an example of cost-consciousness, one case comes to mind in which a plant superintendent brought a problem to a research group while the group leader was away. The group was composed of capable young men and they started to work on the problem, which involved improvement in a chlorination process. When the group leader returned, he was told about the problem and the progress that had been made toward solving it. He asked some questions, which revealed that the entire cost in the step under investigation was only three cents a pound, whereas the organic intermediate used as a starting material in the process cost twelve cents a pound. His reaction was, "Hell, we're working on the wrong problem!" The market for the product was not large and so saving a small fraction of three cents a pound would not pay for much research time.

7) *Relationships:*

The next step in arranging the information at hand in an orderly fashion is to consider the relationships between variables. It is time to analyze logically, and if possible, mathematically, the relation of the variables and the known facts relating to the problem. If the researcher is weak in mathematics, he will do well to have a mathematician examine the relationship between the known variables.

It is sometimes helpful to write down the *dimensional analy-*

sis* of the quantities used. Such an analysis can often give insight into a problem. It can indicate what must be learned by experimentation, and what relations are already known *a priori*. As a matter of fact, natural laws are unavoidable consequences of the nature of the physical quantities involved, as described in their dimensional formulae.

Dimensional analysis is also useful in segregating parts of very complex problems. Partial solution and inner relationships can be worked out, and these give insight into how best to design experiments for final solution of the problem and indicate the relative importance of different variables. The researcher would do well to practice the use of dimensional analysis until it becomes second nature to him. Other values obtained from use of dimensional analysis are given in the book, *Dimensional Analysis*,[1] by H. E. Huntley.

Pure *vs.* Applied Research

But what about pure research as contrasted with applied research? Can a dollar-and-cents judgment be placed on it? First, there is need to examine the meaning of *pure* or *fundamental research* and how it differs from *applied research*. Many per-

---

* Dimensional analysis consists of representing each factor of an expression or equation in terms of the fundamental units of mass, length, time, temperature, etc. A dimensional analysis of the equation for the surface tension in capillary rise, for example, shows that surface tension has the dimension of force per unit length—dynes per centimeter in the *cgs* system.

$$s = \tfrac{1}{2} \, hdgr$$

s = surface tension
h = high of capillary rise = l for length
d = density = ml^{-3}
g = gravitational constant = lt^{-2}
r = radius = l

Substituting the dimensions for each term gives:

$$s = l \times ml^{-3} \times lt^{-2} \times l = mt^{-2}$$

But,

Force, $F = mlt^{-2}$, and dividing both sides by unit length gives

$$\frac{F}{l} = \frac{mt^{-2}}{l} = mt^{-2}$$

Hence, $s = Fl^{-1} = mt^{-2}$

[1] Rinehart & Company, Inc., 1955.

sons that should know better have the notion that pure research is not directed to any practical problem; that it is directed at some theoretical, intangible result which, at best, can have only cultural value. Nothing could be farther from the truth. Most scientific research, in or out of universities, is initiated to solve some very real, practical problem.

Here are a few examples that come to mind:

> When Langmuir set out on his studies of surface films, he was really trying to make a cheaper, more durable light bulb. In sizing up the troubles with the then existing bulbs, he realized that he had to have more facts, more fundamental facts. He had to create new tools with which to solve the problems of the emission of light from a hot surface. It was only incidental that the extensive information and theories that he developed on surface films and absorption also proved to be valuable tools in many other branches of science and engineering.

Or, think of Johann Kepler and calculus, of which Zechariah Chafee, Jr., in his book *The Inquiring Mind*,[2] gives this account:

> Kepler, who was primarily an astronomer, also had an active interest in maintaining a fine vineyard and in the making of wine. The big grape crop of 1613 found him short of wine casks. Suitable wood for wine casks was scarce, and Kepler turned his attention to the task of designing a cask that would hold the *maximum* quantity of wine but require the *minimum* amount of wood. Motivated by this very everyday problem, Kepler became interested in the problem of *maxima* and *minima*. Two and a half years later he published a brochure on the *Scientific Measurement of Wine Casks*, and this classical treatise became the foundation of *infinitesimal calculus*.

In like manner, Professor F. E. Bartell had some real and practical problems in mind when he developed the fundamental equations for measuring adhesion-tension and wetting characteristics. Kekulé was interested in making synthetic dyes when he worked out his theory of ring structure in organic chemistry. One might go on and on with such illustrations. Very probably in each case, if we could know the whole story, we would discover that even the most theoretical researchers had some very practical, everyday problem in mind when they initiated their research.

---

2 Harcourt, Brace & Co., 1928.

What, then, is the difference between so-called fundamental and applied research? C. F. Kettering credits Dr. Urey with the statement that "the difference is *about twenty years*"; i.e., it takes twenty years longer for the results of basic research to find commercial use. Certainly the time interval is one significant difference. So-called fundamental research is broader in scope and usually carries the whole section of the science forward to a new bench mark of knowledge. Applied research is apt to be more restricted in scope and to involve engineering applications of existing scientific knowledge.

If the time span to point of application and breadth of scope are the real differences, and if all serious research is directed ultimately to the serving of human wants and needs, then consideration of cost is surely as applicable to fundamental research as it is to developmental research. The value of a possible solution should be weighed against the costs.

The foregoing may seem to suggest that a frugal, almost miserly, attitude toward spending for research is of first importance. Certainly, if the objective is to commercialize a product or process, cost-accounting is in order at each step, but it is dangerous to be too "dollar-wise" in some kinds of research. By contrast, if the objective is to gain knowledge to broaden some field of science and acquire more fundamental insight, then more *faith* and patient money must be applied.

IV. Propose Likely Solution

Up to this point the researcher has clarified the objective, collected information, and arranged it in an orderly fashion. Now he is ready to propose a method of solving the problem based on the information at hand. At this point he must apply *superior judgment* in drawing deductions from the facts at hand, and use originality and *skill at synthesis* to develop hypotheses.

Points of Departure

Pending more intensive discussion of creative thinking, it will be sufficient at this point merely to list a few simple suggestions to improve ideation.

1) Seek ideas through discussion. Talking a problem over

with others frequently stimulates the individual to thinking of points that had not occurred to him before. Therefore, frequent discussions of a problem are desirable.

2) Seek ideas from purposeful thinking. Actually, in all probability the results obtained in this subjective process are directly related to the time and effort put into thinking about the problem. It is doubtful that research problems are generally solved while discussing ball games or daydreaming. There is, however, one important apparent exception, which will be discussed in the next chapter.

3) Write down ideas as they occur (carry notebook or cards).

4) Compare with analogies.

5) Practice the attitude that it can be done; the question is not WHETHER, but HOW.

V. Test Hypothesis with New Experimental Facts

Once a proposed solution or hypothesis has been conceived, it must be tested. As all the known facts have been used to construct the hypothesis, it can be tested only by some new facts. Experiments must be run to get these new facts. Experienced research men have developed many techniques or "tricks of the trade" which tend to maximize the results from the tests to be run.

Proved Laboratory Techniques

In the long history of scientific development, much attention has been devoted to laboratory technique. A whole body of know-how has been developed, much of it published in articles and books, some of it passed on from professor to student, like folklore. As the complexity of laboratory technique has grown and the principles have become better understood, more and more specific instructions can be given to the young scientist. E. Bright Wilson, Jr., in *An Introduction to Scientific Research*,[3] treats this whole subject of experimental methods so completely and comprehensively that every researcher should carefully study his book. Even though it is written primarily for those in the physical sciences, the social scientist would find much of value for him also.

---

3 McGraw-Hill Book Company, New York, 1952.

Although a full discussion of the many fine points of good experimental technique is beyond the scope of this book, it will be valuable to review briefly some of the more basic ideas. The following comments will be at least a good introduction to the subject.

1) *Make Every Experiment Quantitative Within the Limits of the Equipment Used:*

This means that even in a "test tube" experiment, data should be recorded to the nearest cubic centimeter or gram. Even if you have to guess at the quantities, your guess will be better at the time than the next day or the next month. Many hours of time are sometimes wasted trying to duplicate a successful preliminary test because no quantitative data were recorded.

2) *Account for all Products:*

Attention should be given to heat and material balances, at least crudely, even at the "test tube" stage. Gaseous products, residues, etc., must be measured and accounted for. In some one of the early runs an effort should be made to identify as many of the products as possible and determine the relative quantities of each.

3) *Use Variance Analysis to Determine the Controlling or Critical Variable:*

The modern development of statistics has given the scientist a new, powerful tool to increase efficiency in setting up and analyzing experiments. By properly arranging the experiments, changing several variables over a comparatively small number of experiments and applying *variance analysis* to the results, the controlling variable and its approximate effect can be ascertained. Experiments should be designed or laid out with the use of variance analysis in mind.

A most excellent discussion of this procedure can be found in Chapters 4 and 8 of Wilson's book, *An Introduction to Scientific Research.*[3]

4) *Eliminate all Variables but One:*

In experiments where variance analysis is not to be used, change only one variable at a time. Where in doubt about the ability to control all variables but one, it is desirable to run a blank. If several variables are to be investigated, change the variables according to a pattern.

5) *Arrange to Cancel Uncontrolled Variables:*

Frequently, the conditions of a test can be arranged so as to cancel or minimize unknown or uncontrolled variables; e.g., the accepted methods of sampling.

6) *Make Experiment Independent of Size and Nature of Equipment:*

Obtain more clean-cut and useful data from the experiment by measuring basic data from which specific solutions can be calculated, and by isolating the chemical or physical principles of the problem from the equipment problem. For example, in a problem that involves distillation, first determine data on vapor-liquid equilibrium and then calculate the size of the still required for the given separation.

7) *Equipment:*

Keeping the research equipment simple is an aid to getting clean-cut answers more quickly. A good job of *problem breakdown,* as described in Section III, will aid in determining the kind of equipment needed. Make the development of equipment a separate problem. Attempts to use scale models sometimes introduce variables related to size, which are hard to estimate. One reason is that volume changes as the cube $(V = l^3)$, whereas area changes only as the square $(A = l^2)$.

8) *Plan Maximum Opportunity for Chance:*

Even under the best of conditions there are likely to be unknown variables. Sometimes these have only secondary effects; in other cases, they may profoundly affect the experiment. The experiment should be arranged so as to give the greatest opportunity to note any unusual effect. Some methods that contribute to this are:

a) Use glass equipment whenever it is suitable, to permit visual inspection during operation;

b) Take extra data to permit additional correlations—record any unusual occurrence during the experiment;

c) Maintain an open mind at all times;

d) Watch the actual progress of the experiment *personally*. There is an increasing tendency for trained researchers to turn over the actual running of the experiments to laboratory assistants. If this is done, the trained research man should "stay with the project" where he can inspect and observe the experiment frequently.

9) *Carefully Select the Variables to be Measured:*

Other things being equal, measure the variable that gives a direct and vital answer to the problem. More often than not, other things are not equal, and one should select the variable or variables that can be measured most easily with the required accuracy. For example, it may be easier to measure the change in conductivity of a wire and calculate the change in temperature, than to measure the change in temperature itself.

10) *Observe and Record all Results:*

It sometimes happens that the most significant data from an experiment are the ones that at first appear to be in error. Hence, *all* data, good or bad, expected or unexpected, should be recorded.

11) *Determine Limits of Accuracy:*

Evaluate and record the limits of accuracy on measurements at the time the apparatus is being assembled and the experiments run.

12) *Make Every Experiment Count:*

The laboratory worker should husband his time, fully realizing how valuable it really is. As the experiment progresses, reconsider and answer the following questions: In the light of these new data, is it necessary to complete the planned series of tests? Is this experiment a "stall" while awaiting a better idea? Is this a preliminary experiment which may be unnecessary when the key experiment is run? If in doubt about the objective or value of any laboratory run, it may be time for a little more plain hard thinking.

13) *Make Every Experiment a Safe One:*

The researchers working on atomic energy have set a very high standard for safety which challenges all researchers. In their hazardous field, they have had very few mishaps. If an experiment cannot be made safe, it probably is not worth doing. If it can be made safe, there is no excuse for not doing so.

Serendipity

Many creative scientists have stressed the importance and value of *serendipity*—the exciting occurrence of finding useful or agreeable ideas or experiences that were not being sought. Often, the important advances in science and other disciplines come unexpectedly. An experiment fails, or an unusual and unexpected result is obtained, and to the alert researcher this may start a new train of thought that leads to a new and important discovery. The key here is that the researcher must retain at all times a sensitive curiosity which is stimulated to examine these unexpected results. Moreover, his interest and perspective must be broad enough to visualize the possible social or scientific significance of the unusual fact that the discovery may portend.

The literature is full of examples of chance discoveries that became more valuable than the problem of the original research. There are, no doubt, also many instances—usually not reported—in which a researcher had an important discovery within his grasp but overlooked it because his concentration on the project of the moment blocked his curiosity, or his perspective was too narrow. The late professor of physics, G. T. R. Evans, tells of such an experience early in his career. J. E. Kerrich[4] states of Professor Evans:

> . . . He used to tell his students about an experiment where he was trying to pass an electrical current through a chemical solution. The current would pass in one direction but not in the other. He noticed that one of the electrodes was dirty and polished it, and then the current would pass happily in either direction. Years later he read of an important new discovery: an oxide that permitted a current to pass in one direction but resisted its passage in the other direction.

One cannot stress too much the importance of remaining alert and even actually looking for any unusual results. These should always be noted and examined enough to see whether

---

[4] J. E. Kerrich, University of Witwatersrand, Random Remarks, *The American Statistician*, page 20, June 1961.

it may not be a clue to new and valuable information. But no one should count on leaving anything to chance.[5]

VI. Take Action—Sell Results of Research

Reevaluate Objective

In the light of the additional data obtained from the experiments, the objective can be reevaluated and the breakdown in Section III checked for accuracy. In a sense, this completes the cycle back to the objective. If the research has been successful, the new facts and the proved hypothesis make reconsideration of the objective desirable. Maybe the objective needs to be broadened or changed.

In any case, the next task is to put the results to work. This may involve making them available for other scientists to use or it may involve reporting them to the management of a company to get authorization to commercialize the results. In either case, it involves writing a report.

Write a Good Report

The most important single step in a program of putting research results to work is the formal research report. Whether or not the objective was fully attained, a report should be written covering the progress and results of the experiments. The writing of a report does much to help clarify the objective and the interrelations of factors bearing on the problem. The report is the purposeful recording of the results; and, "If an experiment is worth doing, it is worth taking time to record it."

Although the research report should be factual as to both data and spirit, this does not mean that it must of necessity be dry and uninteresting, or that it should be completely devoid of persuasion. Having merely stated the problem here, let us postpone a more detailed discussion of report writing until Chapter 4.

APPLYING THE SIX-STEP METHOD

Some of the steps in applying the six-step scientific method are hard to explain. A few examples will help clarify some of

---

[5] Bernard E. Schaar, Serendipity—A comedy of errors, *Chemist,* 35:411-418; 456 (1958).

the points. The solutions as given are for real problems, but the reader will derive the most good in studying through the method by working out problems familiar to himself. Let us begin by looking at a problem that developed about the end of World War II.

PROBLEM I

PREPARATION OF DICHLOROSTYRENE

About 1945, some test results on synthetic rubber made from butadiene and dichlorostyrene looked very good, and there was some thought of substituting dichlorostyrene for the styrene regularly used in the government's program for synthetic rubber. If such a change were to be made, it would be desirable to have the "dichlor" process fit into the styrene plants then owned by the government. The problem was farmed out by the Rubber Reserve Corporation to two different laboratory groups, each of which was well versed in chemical separations by distillation.

Let us apply our outline to this problem. First, we shall state the objective. In stating the objective it quickly became evident that the *immediate objective* was to find an azeotrope for separating dichlorostyrene and dichloroethylbenzene and other products of the dehydrogenated mixture. Both laboratories working on this problem concluded from preliminary analysis that this step would be a real and major problem in the project.

State Objective

1) Develop a commercial process for economic, large-scale production of dichlorostyrene.
2) Find an azeotropic agent that would make purification by distillation a possibility.

Assemble Facts

The following is a list of facts that seem pertinent to the problem:

1) Dichloroethylbenzene can be dehydrogenated over a catalyst in the same way that ethylbenzene can be dehydrogenated to styrene.
2) The effluent from the dehydrogenator is a mixture of all the three isomers of dichlorostyrene, the three chloroethylbenzenes, and a number of decomposition isomers.
3) The lowest-boiling isomer of dichlorostyrene appears to have a boiling point at best only 0.5 to 1°C above the highest-boiling dichloroethylbenzene.
4) The rate of polymerization of dichlorostyrene is about ten times that of styrene at a given temperature.

5) The normal polymerization inhibitors are effective but give a much shorter induction period with dichlorostyrene.

6) The boiling points of azeotropic mixtures are either higher or lower than that of either component in a two-component system.

7) It is likely that the unsaturated isomers will behave similarly toward any azeotroping agent.

8) Published rules can be used to select classes of compounds that have more tendency to form azeotropes with unsaturated compounds than with saturated ones.[6]

9) Laboratory samples of dichlorostyrene and dichloroethylbenzene of satisfactory purity can be prepared by direct distillation.

Make Breakdown of Problem

Ordinarily, the first requirement would be to make a list of steps. As assigned, however, this problem had already been broken down into steps. The step under consideration here consisted in separating and purifying the compound after dehydrogenation.

The next requirement, then, was to outline an orderly arrangement of information.

1) *Scientific Field Involved:*

The scientific field involved here is phase relations.

2) *Known Major Variables:*

Temperature, Pressure, Composition.

3) *Type of Data Required:*

Data on phase equilibrium are required.

4) *Known Methods:*

A number of kinds of apparatus and procedures have been reported in the literature for obtaining data on phase equilibrium.

5) *Opposites:*

The opposite of separation would be mixing. It is doubtful that much aid would come from considering mixing at this stage.

6) *Cost Factors:*

Analysis by batch distillation not only involved considerable direct labor, but also delay in getting results. Thus, direct costs of running tests to evaluate a particular azeotroping agent would be high and elapsed time would delay results.

---

[6] R. H. Ewell: Azeotropic Distillation, *Ind. Eng. Chem.*, 36(10):871-874 (1944).

Likely Method of Solving Problem

Now we have come to the crucial step. If this were your problem what would you do? How would you propose to find the azeotroping agent that will separate this mixture? You would select likely compounds by applying the azeotroping rules. Yes, then what? How would you go about picking the particular compound or compounds that would be effective in the given problem?

Two different laboratories did attack this problem by running a series of batch distillations—the first as a blank, the subsequent ones each with a different azeotroping agent. By comparing the analyses of different cuts from these batch distillations with the corresponding cuts from the blank, the researchers could decide whether an azeotrope had actually formed. To complete each batch distillation required about 24 hours of elapsed time, followed by analysis of the double-bond content of several of the cuts. To test one hundred possible azeotroping agents by this method would require several months of operators' time (costly in dollars) and several months of lapsed time (costly in extending the research period).

Now let us go back and look at all the facts we put down under *Assemble Facts* in our general outline. The only fact that the procedure first outlined did not utilize was No. 6—the fact that azeotropic boiling points are either lower or higher than that of either component. When one brings this pertinent information to bear on the problem, he quickly realizes that a boiling range will answer the question of azeotrope or no azeotrope very certainly. In actual practice, a boiling-range apparatus of 10cc capacity was used and a possible agent could be tested in about twenty minutes. Results could be obtained on a hundred likely azeotroping agents in a few days.

This problem has been tried on a number of groups. Each time, some member of the group has come up with this neat procedure in less than one minute after the facts were put on the board. This was true even in one group of graduate students who had had no practical experience either with styrene or with distillation, but who knew physical chemistry.

PROBLEM II

MIXING OF FLUIDS

Let us look at another problem, which does not have to do with separations. This problem is to develop a satisfactory method of continuously mixing two streams of molten plastics. Some researchers attack this problem by thinking out a mixing machine and then building a pilot-plant-sized model to test the idea.

Another researcher, reasoning along the lines of the outline set down for Problem I, obtained his answer with almost no expenditure of dollars and in a matter of a few hours. Let us analyze this problem by the same outline.

State Objective

1) To mix continuously two or more streams of molten plastics.
2) To design a machine to do the mixing.

Assemble Facts:

1) Molten plastics are viscous liquids.
2) Viscosity is a function of temperature.
3) Adhesion between hot plastics and metals is sufficient to cause laminar flow at low displacements.
4) In the regions of turbulence, mixing will occur without the aid of direction changers, such as paddles.

Following the orderly arrangement of information,

1) *Scientific Field:*

Fluid flow and mixing.

2) *Variables:*

Viscosity and velocity.

3) *Type of Data Required:*

Rate of shear to give turbulent flow.

Known Methods:

One might list as known methods for mixing: Mechanical agitation, turbulent flow, supersonic waves, diffusion.

Skip (5) *Opposites* and (6) *Cost Factors* for the moment and go on to relationships. A little reflection at this point brings to mind the fact that the known relationship (laminar and turbulent flow) is specified by Reynolds number, which shows the relationship between rate of flow, velocity, and density.

Proposed Likely Solution

With all the assembled facts in mind, the researcher proposed as a solution that the molten streams of plastic be passed through the annular space between a smooth, elongated, concentric rotor and stator. To test his proposed solution he proceeded as follows:

He dissolved some clear plastic in a high-boiling liquid to form a concentrated solution with a viscosity equal to that of the molten plastic at the temperatures used for processing. He then filled a petri dish with this solution. The petri dish that was used had a flat bottom about 15 cm in diameter and vertical sides about 2 cm high. He then placed a drop of oil-soluble dye on the surface of the solution at the center of the dish. He next covered the petri dish with a large glass plate in such a way as to avoid introducing an air bubble, and then inverted the dish and glass plate as a unit.

1) By moving the inverted petri dish on the glass, he could observe the movement of the color throughout the mass enclosed by the petri dish.
2) By changing the size of the petri dish, using others with sides of different heights, he could simulate different wall separations.
3) By changing the speed at which the petri dish was moved over the glass plate, he could evaluate the effect of rate of shear.
4) By the distance the petri dish had to be moved to effect mixing, he could evaluate the rate of mixing.

With this simple device he was able to obtain sufficient engineering data to design the desired mixing machine.

It is interesting to note that in both of the cases cited, the laboratory experiment was set up to exclude questions related to the design of specific equipment. As a consequence, the experiments and apparatus were simple and cheap, and led to direct and useful answers.

Problem III
A MATTER OF WEIGHING

In breaking down any problem, keep in mind the many routes that are possible. If there are two or more steps in the process, there are many routes by virtue of combination.

A good illustration is the ancient problem of comparing coins. Assume that there are twelve coins and that it is known that one coin is either light or heavy. The problem is to ascertain, in the least number of trials, which coin is the odd one and whether it is heavy or light; and to do this with a balance but without using weights.

Proposed Likely Solution

1st Step

1. Divide the 12 coins into four piles (three in each)
2. Balance pile 1 against pile 2:
   a) If balanced, then the odd coin is in pile 3 or 4.
3. Next balance pile 3 against pile 4.
   a) If they do not balance, note which is heavier.
   b) If the left pan is heavier, then there is:
      1) A heavy coin on the left side, or
      2) A light coin on the right side.

2nd Step

4. Remove coins 7, 8 and 9 from the left pan, and substitute coins 1, 2 and 3, previously weighed.
   a) If the pans now balance, then coin 7, 8, or 9 is heavy.
5. Balance coin 7 against coin 8:
   a) If they balance, then coin 9 is heavy;
   Otherwise, the heavy coin goes down.
   b) If the left pan is still heavy, then coin 10, 11, or 12 is light.
6. Balance coin 10 against coin 11:
   a) If they balance, then coin 12 is light;
   Otherwise, the light coin goes up.

Notes: The key here to a correct method of attack resides in:
1. Make no weighing which did not give new information; e.g., weighing 6 coins against 6 would give no new knowledge. One already knew the odd coin would be in one of the groups of six.
2. The knowledge that three is the largest group from which the odd coin can be selected by a single weighing and that if one knows from previous weighing, whether heavy or light, one weighing will specify one of given three.

SUMMARY

The solving of problems is one of the commonest of human experiences. Every day brings many choices, many decisions, each of them a problem. Most of these are small ones of little consequence, but occasionally a problem stands out in opportunity and challenge like a shooting star, pointing the way to progress. Nor is man an unwilling victim of problems. He is wont to seek them out, forever asking questions of *what* and *where* and *when*, and *why* and *how* and *who*.

Because problems, great and small, are so commonplace, most persons try to solve them in a sort of "second nature",— almost haphazard—approach, rather than by a carefully planned procedure. Some individuals discovered by trial and error an effective technique for solving problems and thus gained recognition as outstanding thinkers; but even many scientific researchers have failed to develop an orderly approach. The experimental procedures that were developed in the 17th and 18th centuries, which came to be known as the *scientific method*, were a big step forward in applying a systematic approach to the solving of problems. Unfortunately, even many scientists have never been fully instructed in the scientific method, and hence, they do not apply it effectively. In the drive for greater productivity, it is time to turn our attention again to the methodology of problem-solving.

The six-step procedure for a more efficient technique, which is set forth in this chapter and elaborated in subsequent chapters, is an attempt to outline more clearly the application of the scientific method. The method has been presented in the setting of scientific research problems. Actually, it is equally suited to all kinds—business problems, government problems, or personal problems. In fact, what has come to be called "Operations Research", as applied in military and business organizations, is merely the extension of the scientific method into these fields.

One of the advantages of studying the six-step method and applying it is that after repeated use this systematic approach will become a habit. At this stage we shall automatically apply it to all problems and thus improve our effectiveness. Such an approach to personal problems, for example, would greatly reduce worry and indecision. Moreover, the habit of consistently using the systematic approach to problems will make any individual more effective in all types of contacts, on the job and in the community.

To gain these advantages, how should this book be used? This will, of course, depend a great deal on the individual. For many, it will be desirable after a first reading to turn back and study through Chapter 2 again, giving special attention to the six steps. By a suitable technique the steps should be so thoroughly learned that they automatically come to mind whenever a problem arises.

Practice Good Procedure

There is the constant temptation to jump right into a new problem. The hardest part will be to fix the habit of *always* stopping to clarify the objective.

First of all, we need to firmly fix in mind these six steps:

1. STATE THE OBJECTIVE
2. ASSEMBLE THE FACTS
3. ORGANIZE THE FACTS
4. PROPOSE LIKELY SOLUTION
5. TEST THE SOLUTION
6. TAKE ACTION—SELL RESULTS

Next comes the practice—the application of the procedure to actual problems. At first, this will take some checking back to review some of the hints and key points that are suggested. After a few trials the procedure will become more or less automatic. Subsequently, when a problem proves stubborn it may be helpful to think through the steps carefully or even to check back to make sure that each step is being fully applied. In this way, good habits of problem-solving will become second nature.

As the solving of problems is such a constant part of living, good technique should be learned young. Training in home and school generally does not suffice. This is due in part to lack of emphasis on the technique of problem-solving but also in part, to immaturity. The young adult has to develop some self-reliance and experience in facing problems before he is prepared to give attention to technics and methodology. After he has been baffled a few times and has made some bad decisions, he may arrive at the "disturbed state" and become receptive. For this reason the latter part of college might be an ideal time to introduce formal instruction on the solving of problems.

In the middle 1940's the Detroit Economics Club sent a questionnaire to large employers of college graduates in Michigan. Most of the answers, whether from industrial management, bankers, or the service industries, carried the common complaint: Most college graduates were at a complete loss when faced with a problem. They did not even know how to tackle the problem, let alone how to carry it forward to a solution. Managers had found that college training did not equip most students to meet and solve problems. The new employee had to be given this training on the job. It appears that in addition to courses in subject matter, colleges could improve their product by giving specific instruction in methods of solving problems.

As the absolute minimum, those students that continue into graduate school should have instruction in the technique of solving problems before they are allowed to begin research for an advanced degree. One approach would be to set up a seminar on the technique of problem-solving and make it a prerequisite to starting a research project. The discussion type of presentation has been used successfully in seminars to introduce the six-step method described here to both industrial researchers and graduate students. A manual can be prepared which can be used by the discussion leader, and this, with suitable modification, should be widely applicable wherever the presentation is to be made by the discussion technique. An alternative method might use this book as a text, and devote some of the class periods to practice in solving practical problems.

Although college probably is the natural place to teach good habits of problem-solving, it will no doubt be years before even most science majors are fully introduced to the finer points of the scientific method. Accordingly, industry will need to fill the gap. As a systematic approach to good problem-solving techniques, industry could use seminars on the six-step method as part of the training course for young recruits.

Another use suggests itself for the six-step method. Larger research organizations might from time to time assemble a group of researchers with diverse training and rigorously apply the six-step method to some of the tough problems that confront the organization. In other words, a systematic procedure for problem-solving could be added to the team approach.

The social changes that result from rapid industrial advancement and the impact of science, expanding exponentially, has greatly multiplied the personal problems of adjustment. The use of good problem-solving techniques will help the individual to keep up with the fast pace of change. He will be better able to meet change and, in his work efforts, to bring about constructive change more efficiently. It is time to adopt and apply regularly the six-step systematic procedure for solving problems.

chapter 3

CREATIVE THINKING

The real essence of problem-solving is the creative thinking given as step 4 in Chapter 2, namely, proposing the likely solution. In fact, the very core of the *scientific method* is the creation of a hypothesis that correlates the known facts, and which, if proved by further experimentation, can be used to predict future events involving the given variables. The previous steps in the proposed procedure are merely preliminary; they set the stage. Now you may ask, "Is there really anything we can do to improve our results in this area?" Let us examine this more fully and see what can be done to improve this part of the problem-solving process.

It is possible, even probable, that creative thinkers are born, not made; that some persons have a natural aptitude for it. In the creative thinker there may be a greater tendency for the nerve impulses that accompany thought to shunt across previously unused synapses and thus establish new thought paths or patterns. This may be due to a slightly different chemical or physical makeup of the brain. If so, the tendency would be largely controlled by heredity.

One thing is certain, however. Whether inherited talent is large or small, most individuals are using it to only a small fraction of capacity. If this is true, it should be possible through proper training to improve performance in creative thinking. The ordinary educational processes are not notably successful in developing creativity; in fact, they may repress it. Many highly trained individuals are sterile so far as new ideas are concerned. Others, like Edison, accomplish outstanding results without much formal training. Although formal education is necessary to give the individual habits of learning and skill in communication, as well as a background of facts and theories, it cannot be expected to develop the skill for creative thinking in the same way that it teaches facts.

CREATIVITY AS A MENTAL PROCESS

In the past two decades, considerable attention has been given to the problem of whether creativity can be improved, and if so, how. Large companies—for example, General Electric—have developed training courses for new scientists and engineers which they hope will improve their performance in research and development. A number of university researchers have investigated various aspects of creativity. These studies have clearly shown that creativity can be improved. They have also suggested useful techniques for developing originality. A rather considerable literature has now accumulated on the measurement and detection of creativity and on techniques for better performance. In *A Source Book for Creative Thinking*,[1] Sidney J. Parnes and Harold F. Harding have assembled a large number of papers and reports on researches on creativity during the past decade. Among them are papers by many of the outstanding researchers in this field.

At one time, interest in the mental processes was centered largely on IQ measurements. It is now clear that such measurements give, at best, a one-dimensional evaluation, and that the intellect is actually multidimensional. In addition to creative ability, J. P. Guilford, of the University of Southern California, lists reasoning, evaluation, planning, and problem-solving. In studying creativity, he hypothesized that it might involve seven distinct abilities, namely:

1) Sensing a problem that calls for solution;
2) Fluency of thinking (ideas per minute);
3) Flexibility;
4) Originality;
5) Analyzing;
6) Synthesizing;
7) Redefining the problem.

---

[1] Sidney J. Parnes and Harold F. Harding, *A Source Book for Creative Thinking;* Charles Scribner's Sons, New York, 1962.

Studies on factor-analysis supported this view. In fact, it began to be clear that the intellect, or mental ability, is a very complicated process. Coordination of data from extensive researches led Professor Guilford to group the factors of intellect under three dimensions:

1) The kind of operation performed;
2) The kind of material or content involved;
3) The kind of products.

Under each of these dimensions he lists subdivisions, and relates them through the three-dimensional grid shown in Figure 3:1.

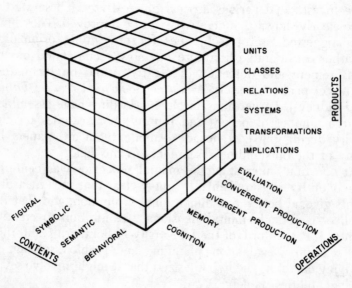

Fig. 3:1 THEORETICAL MODEL FOR COMPLETE "STRUCTURE OF INTELLIGENCE" PROJECT ON APTITUDES OF HIGH-LEVEL PERSONNEL
Department of Psychology, University of Southern California,
June, 1960

From this type of correlation it becomes clear that originality is the ability to produce a variety of transformations and that some individuals are more apt in handling symbols, others in handling ideas, and still others in handling transformations of special or concrete objects. Various types of mental ability can be placed in the grid system. For example, the factor that is called "expressional fluency" would reside in the area specified as "ability to produce *divergent, symbolic systems.*"

It appears that most creative abilities would be classed in the category of divergent thinking. An exception appears to be ability for redefinition, which must be classified as "convergent thinking." The factor that was labeled "sensitivity to problems" falls in the category of "evaluation."

Even a casual examination would lead to the conclusion that IQ tests touch upon only a very few factors of the intellect. Such tests generally are dominated by one factor, that of verbal comprehension—the ability to recognize semantic units. This overemphasis on the ability to know verbal concepts has placed a premium on those attributes that are primarily useful only in the academic environment, and it accounts for the lack of high correlation between IQ rating and creativity.

The grid system that Professor Guilford has proposed takes on increased meaning if we think of the mental process as a type of computer system. In retrieval, for example, some minds may have stored information more clearly labeled by symbols, others by ideas, and still others by, let's say, a physical image —that is, the three-dimensional structural aspect. In memory then, depending on which was the dominant code, the individual could recall one type of information more readily than another. Other processes, such as comparing and evaluating, classifying, etc., would depend, in a sense, on the way the mind codes the stored information. This may well account for a rather common difference in individuals, whereby some learn and remember easily logical concepts and systems, but have difficulty with random or uncoordinated facts, while others show an opposite aptitude.

As a frame of reference, it will be helpful first to examine the individual as a whole and some general characteristics which are related to this abstract subject. This will be followed by a discussion of some of the techniques that have been found useful in improving originality and creativity. In addition to the strictly mental factors, there appear to be other traits which are essential to an effective use of the creative processes.

TRAITS OF CREATIVE THINKERS

Using data from a study by Walter B. Pitkin, William H. Easton[2] arrived at the following list. The creative thinker must have:

1. Ambition
2. Perseverance
3. Enthusiasm
4. Energy
5. Fund of knowledge (experience)
6. An inquiring mind (creativity, imagination).

1. Ambition

Ambition is listed first, probably because of its importance as an emotional factor, for it is required to get the individual started on purposeful projects. Many individuals have good intentions, even ideas and plans, but never get started on a project. There is both a long-range and a short-range factor in getting started. The long-range factor spoken of as "ambition" consists of a sort of personal integration toward a long-range objective. Not just any objective, but rather one that results in increased position relative to one's associates. It is this integration that causes one to forego present pleasures for the prospect of future ones. We say of such a person that he has a *long-range view.*

A short-range emotional factor is also important. The psychologists speak of it as the "disturbed state." Bichowsky,[3] in his book, *Industrial Research,* says that the individual not only must be faced with a problem, but also must be required to do something about it. He must be disturbed, uneasy, uncomfortable about it. When the surroundings are too comfortable, there is a human tendency to "vegetate." Under such conditions, creative thinking does not flourish.

2. Perseverance

Perseverance is needed because creative thinking is not easy. Generally, the desired results do not come quickly. Success is apt to come only after repeated trials.

[2] William H. Easton, Creative thinking and how to develop it, *Mechanical Engineering,* August 1946.
[3] F. R. Bichowsky, *Industrial Research;* Chemical Publishing Company, Brooklyn, N.Y., 1942.

Society so heralds the final success that we often forget the many failures that preceded it. Perseverance implies more than a kind of rational doggedness. In two ways, failure may be used as stepping-stones to ultimate success. First of all, even though the attempt was not successful, nevertheless, experience and background are being built. The researcher is increasing his total accumulated store of knowledge about the problem. It is a new deposit in the sum of knowledge against which the creative mental processes may draw in developing the successful idea or solution. Moreover, study and analysis of each failure will, at the very least, indicate approaches to be avoided. It is this constructive attitude that is implied in the perseverance that the creative thinker needs.

3. Enthusiasm

New ideas do not present themselves to an unwilling worker. Enthusiasm serves as a mental stimulant and opens wide the gates to new ideas. The individual that lacks enthusiasm for the project and does not enjoy creativity cannot expect to be really creative.

Thought processes involve nervous impulses that flow along one nerve fiber to a synapse and there activate another nerve cell. Not all impulses jump a synapse and activate the adjoining cell. Each cell at any given time has a *threshold value* below which it does not respond. The threshold value may be varied in many ways—by electric currents or fields, and by chemical environment. The amount of oxygen or carbon dioxide in the blood, and the concentration of salts, can influence the threshold. Some chemicals and drugs, such as strychnine, lower the threshold. Others in the form of sedatives and anesthetics raise the threshold.

Adrenalin or *epinephrine*, the hormone produced by the adrenal glands, which is liberated when the organism is under stress or faces an emergency, lowers the threshold of the nerve cells and makes them more receptive to activation. Too much epinephrine can upset the balance to the place where constructive processes of thought or action may be thwarted. A modest increase in epinephrine, however, lowers the threshold and increases the flow of nervous impulses. Clearly this can facilitate the process of ideation.

The mental processes also seem to accommodate in subtle ways to concern, attention, interest, and dedication. Feedback from attitudes in some subtle way influences the threshold of the synapse, and thus, the flow of nerve impulses. Enthusiasm and a degree of optimism are an emotional multiplier— a sort of catalyst to creative effort.

4. Energy

Intense mental effort is required for creative thinking. Although this does not require a strong physical body, it does seem to require a good physical tone. Dissipation, which throws the bodily functions out of rhythm, is sure to decrease creative capacity. There is a strong tendency for those engaged in mental work to neglect the exercise of the physical body. Most normal individuals will find their health better and an improved zest for solving problems if they exert themselves physically each day sufficiently to work up a sweat. Such activity flushes out the system, carrying away the chemical decomposition products that accumulate as a result of the mental effort.

Some years ago a chemist friend of mine complained one evening about being tired out at the end of his long, arduous days. He was arising early, commuting about forty miles to work in the heart of Detroit, working eight hours in an industrial laboratory, returning home, and working on a project in his private laboratory after supper. I suggested that what he needed to do was to get out for a three-to-four-mile hike at a fast pace each evening. He was too polite to say much, but later told me he thought me more than a little crazy, as he was already spending most of the day on his feet. Some time later, however, he tried out the suggestion and found it to be an excellent tonic. A brisk walk speeded his heartbeat and breathing, and flushed out some of the accumulated poisons from the activities of the day. An occasional splurge of overexertion will not give the desired results; regular physical exercise is better.

Body Types

The need for physical exercise and the reaction to it will differ, depending on the individual's body type. Studies by

Dr. William H. Sheldon[4] and others indicate that there are three basic body types. Most individuals, however, are not one pure type, but rather are a composite with varying degrees of dominance of one of the types. Sheldon labeled the three types: *Endomorph, Mesomorph,* and *Ectomorph*. If we indicate these pure types as the apexes of a triangle, most individuals would find their particular type located on the plane of the triangle and nearer to one corner in varying degrees; see Figure 3:2.

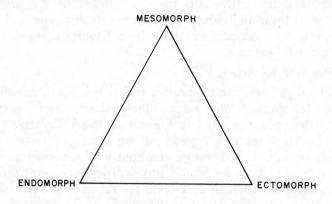

Fig. 3:2 VARIETIES OF HUMAN PHYSIQUE

The true *mesomorph* is the natural athlete. He will have a symmetrical body with heavy bones, thick muscles, and strong connective tissues. The mesomorph has good digestion, eats heartily, and has an abundance of energy. Regular and extensive exercise is vital to good health for such an individual.

The *endomorph* is the rounded or well-padded type. He has small bones, a short neck, and a round head, chest, abdomen, legs, and arms. As he loves food and has a highly efficient digestive tract, he has a tendency to put on excess weight. The endomorph does not have an urge for exercise as does the mesomorph, but he will feel better if he follows a regular program of exercise. He should not exercise violently at irregular

---

[4] William H. Sheldon, *Varieties of Human Physique;* Harper & Brothers, New York, 1940.

intervals, especially if overweight, but should maintain a moderate and regular program.

The *ectomorph* is the long, thin type. His intestine may be as much as ten feet shorter than that of the endomorph, and it is so sensitive that rough or spicy foods may irritate it. Because of the relatively high ratio of body surface to volume and the relative inefficiency of the digestive tract, the ectomorph often has difficulty in maintaining his energy. The true ectomorph may get along quite well with a minimum of physical exertion, but because few individuals are pure ectomorphs, it is probable that even those individuals that approach this type will have better health and physical tone by following a regular program of mild exercise.

5. Store of Knowledge

A vital prerequisite to creative thinking is the accumulation of a vital store of knowledge. Rarely, if ever, does anything completely new come out of the human mind. Creative thinking consists of rearranging and putting together into new combinations, bits of knowledge acquired in the normal manner. A big fund of knowledge and broad experience constitute the ingredients from which new ideas are made. Quite frequently, new discoveries and advances are made in the no-man's land, where two or more branches of science meet. This happens when an individual that is acquainted with the knowledge in both fields develops new concepts and relationships involving knowledge from both of them. In fact, one very fruitful source of discovery and invention is the carrying over of analogies from one field to another.

Anyone that would do creative thinking should constantly seek new experiences and knowledge. He must constantly be engaged in enlarging his store of knowledge by study, experiment, and observation. He must have a high capacity for self-instruction.

6. Creative Imagination

Creative imagination is listed as one of the essential qualifications for creative thinking. Before we discuss this aspect, however, let us consider a related factor. What are the mental tools used by creative thinkers? Are there many kinds of such tools—some used by authors, some by artists, others by musicians, and still others by inventors? No. There is only one set of mental tools used by all creative thinkers. The use of the same mental equipment for a variety of activities explains why Leonardo da Vinci attained superiority in many different fields as he applied his creative skill alternately as a scientist, a painter, a sculptor, a musician, a physician, an inventor, and an engineer. He used the same mental tools in each field, and the problem-solving approach which proved successful in one field could be applied directly in the other fields.

Noncreative Thinking

There is but a single kit of tools for creative thinking, and all are important. But for purposes of examination, they can be divided into two groups—noncreative and creative mental processes.

The *noncreative* mental processes involve:

> Observation
> Reflection
> Memory
> Reasoning
> Judgment

These processes enable the individual to assemble facts, come to certain conclusions relative to the significance of the collected material, and to assess the probable correctness of these conclusions. In other words, these noncreative processes are the *bases* of all logical thought, and hence, are the foundation of all sound creative thinking. Steps 1, 2, and 3 of the procedure outlined in Chapter 2 constitute a systematic procedure for noncreative thinking.

To go beyond the results of noncreative or logical thinking requires the application of the processes and tools of *creative thinking*. With respect to creative thinking, a couple of points need to be made clear. First of all, the creative thinker does not really create something new. He does not "evolve new ideas" but rather new combinations of ideas that are already resident in his mind. Sometimes this involves only long-known ideas. At other times the creative combination will be sparked by a newly acquired idea or fact.

In the second place, the results of creative thinking need not be new. They may be new only to the particular individual. In fact, at some other time or under different circumstances, the same individual might arrive at the same result by logical processes, if for example, he had different or more facts. The difference between noncreative and creative thinking lies in the fact that the former takes place in the conscious mental processes, whereas the latter takes place, at least in part, in the subconscious mind. The chief difference lies in the feeling that we understand the processes of the former, but not those of the latter.

The operation of the mental processes might be likened to modern office machines—calculators and computers. The logical thought processes would seem to be more like those of a calculator—less complex and more understandable. By contrast, creative thinking, which appears to take place in the subconscious mind, would be more like the operations of an electronic computer. Even if the mechanics of each step may be the same, the multiplicity and intricate sequence makes the result seem less comprehensible and almost like magic.

Some now think that the mental processes, including the subconscious ones, do indeed operate like a very large and complicated computer.[5] If this is the case, then constructive thinking and especially creative thinking will reflect the skill with which the given problem is programmed into the mind. Steps 1 and 2, and especially step 3 of Chapter 2, are designed to improve the mental programming of problems.

Types of Creative Thinking

Creative thinking, although less well understood, can be shown to use three fairly well-defined processes. Whether these creative processes differ fundamentally or not, they are unlike in action, results, and controllability. Easton[2] lists and describes the creative processes as follows:

> *Imagination,* which is the power that enables a thinker to weave ideas into new combinations while he is engaged in deliberate thinking. It usually deals with easily remembered ideas.

---

[5] Psycho-cybernetics.

Inspiration, which is the result of an accidental stimulus. It occurs when new ideas derived from some observed object or circumstance suddenly and automatically combine with old ideas.

Illumination, which is evoked by intense deliberate thinking and forms new combinations of ideas after the thinking has ceased. It resembles inspiration in occurring without present effort, but has an entirely different cause. It frequently brings to the surface long-forgotten ideas.

Although these three processes are of major importance for creative thinkers, there may be others that also can give insight and new ideas. William James,[6] after much study, believed that some people have had experiences at times that gave them insight in a manner uncommon to the normal processes of thought.

Moreover, careful studies on clairvoyance have demonstrated beyond question that some individuals have foreknowledge of information in some extrasensory manner when the individual is separated from the fact by either space, time, or both.

Whether visions and clairvoyance are really different from other processes, is unimportant for our purposes. Few individuals appear to have these abilities, and even those that do have them seldom make major contributions in arts or science. In any event, these possible means of insight can safely be ignored as a tool for solving problems at our present state of psychological understanding.

Creative thinkers differ from other persons, not so much in creativity as in the way they use their creative mental processes. Most individuals use their creative processes in random, undirected activities. They daydream, build castles in the air, worry, and devise methods of escaping from trouble. These activities are used to fill in when no other diversion is at hand, or as a disagreeable mental labor under stress of necessity.

The effective creative thinker, by contrast, uses the creative processes deliberately, purposefully, and to specific ends. He enjoys using them. It is a thrilling experience to observe a really effective creative thinker in conversation. Whatever the subject, he is soon examining and handling it as a collector

---

[6] William James, *Variety of Religious Experiences;* Modern Library, 1936.

might examine an antique. He is turning it over to get a new perspective and is likely to suggest new uses or relationships before the conversation goes far. The zest such individuals have for exercising these processes is evident. The creative thinker is not necessarily more intelligent than others; he merely integrates his natural mental processes to useful ends.

It is proper to say *natural mental processes*, for creative thinking appears to be instinctive; no one needs to be instructed in how to exercise his imagination or how to recognize inspiration when it occurs. But the efficient use of the processes is a different matter. Efficiency here means getting results in the minimum of time and with the least expenditure of mental and nervous energy.

TOOLS FOR CREATIVE THINKING

To utilize the tools for creative thinking more effectively, one needs to know:

1) Which process to employ under a given circumstance;
2) The capabilities and limitations of each;
3) The conditions which favor and which inhibit the activity of each process; and
4) How to control each, insofar as possible.

Let us now turn to a consideration of these matters.

Imagination and Deliberate Creative Thinking

Imagination is the handmaid of deliberate creative thinking —thinking that seeks a clearly defined objective through a series of steps. These steps will be determined by the problem, but in all cases the first step is to use imagination to construct from knowledge and experience a concept (outline, framework) which will serve as a basis for further work. As this concept is built by the use of imagination, it is closely supervised by reason. Reason inspects each proposed idea and accepts or rejects it as suitable.

Avoid Judicial Attitude

Physical scientists, in particular, are apt to have developed reason into a zealous, exacting censor. This is often a handicap, sometimes almost a bar, to real creative thinking. Such scientists are the plodders who seldom, if ever, make the intuitive advances that come from real creative thinking. The same principle also applies to writers. It is precisely for this reason that the would-be writer is frequently advised to write his thoughts down as they come, without much attention to form or grammar. The mechanics can be improved later. The application of too much censorship at first inhibits the imagination and flow of ideas. It was to avoid the inhibition caused by censorship that made Osborn[7] rule it out during his "brainstorming" sessions.

The imagination sometimes quickly builds a preliminary framework so complete that the idea can be filled out and completed solely by logical thinking. Such might be the case for a short story conceived in its essential entirety, or an idea for a mechanical device that requires only a working drawing. Creative endeavor, however, is rarely so simple or easy. Most projects are more involved and complicated, and the first creative effort results in an outline or general plan which can then be filled in and completed only by solving many detailed problems. The execution of the completed projects consists finally in solving each of the several problems in turn. These may be many and varied, but they can be divided into the three classes mentioned earlier, depending on the mental process used to handle them. Basically, this classification is determined by the ease with which the individual solves them. The thinker can solve some of these problems offhand from his knowledge and experience, either by use of logical thought or by imagination. A simple step in a purely chemical problem might be solved easily and quickly by a trained chemist, but it might be difficult or even impossible for a lawyer or writer to solve. As soon, however, as the thinker meets a problem that he cannot solve at once, he must turn to the less deliberate creative processes.

Deliberate thinking may thus solve all the problems inherent in the framework laid down, but often some more refractory problems may arise. As these problems are not solved by the thinker's imagination and reasoning power, solution must be sought outside the field of deliberate thinking. This does not necessarily mean that a solution is impossible, for the thinker

---

[7] Alex F. Osborn, *Applied Imagination;* Chas. Scribner's Sons, New York, 1953.

may turn to the mental process called "illumination," or he may be blessed with an inspiration. Before examining these, however, let us examine some of the characteristics of imagination.

Imagination is used in all phases of deliberate creative thinking. In anything but purely routine effort, the imagination is continuously active.

Unfortunately, however, the imagination cannot always be turned off and on at will. Sometimes it is like a young bird dog that for the moment would sooner chase rabbits than point birds.

This independence of the imagination can be troublesome to the creative thinker, for creative thinking on a given project is impossible if the imagination has pressing business elsewhere. One may try again and again to get going on the problem, only to have the mind wander elsewhere. This is very exasperating and some creative thinkers postpone the project until the right mood comes.

Have you ever had days when everything seems to go wrong? This may also be associated with the same sort of wandering of interest and attention. I have been told of a scientist who, if he came to the laboratory and found things going wrong, would go home, sit down at the piano and play—if necessary, for hours—until his mood had changed. He would then go back to the laboratory and work, perhaps well into the night.

Mood does not appear to be so important for successful, logical thought, but in creative thinking the proper mood is a prerequisite. Imagination will occupy itself only with whatever has the strongest emotional appeal of the moment.

Some creative thinkers may adjust their productive efforts to their moods. Many, however, must work at specified times and even meet deadlines. Such thinkers are not completely at the mercy of capricious imagination, however. Control of interest, like will power, can be improved by exercise. He that practices control of interest will be rewarded by increasing self-mastery. Similarly, practice of the habit of defeat and resignation is sure to lead to increasing frustration and lack of concentration. There is a technique that is effective in wooing the interest which is so essential to imagination. A crossword puzzle will serve as an example to illustrate the method.

To Build Interest

Solving a crossword puzzle is of itself pretty much pointless and few persons deliberately set out to solve them. But in an idle moment, if an obvious word is filled in and then one or two others that come easily, interest is aroused and it is likely to be sustained until the puzzle is completed. Or, merely watch one or two moves in a game of solitaire and notice how quickly interest is aroused and sustained, to the point of even wanting to help make the moves.

The same principle can be used to arouse interest in important problems. Random thinking about the problem will not help, and any attempt to force the imagination to obey is useless, but deliberate concentration on, and the solving of, little problems connected with the big one will snare the interest.

Solving some little problem arouses enough interest to lead to another small part of the project, and this in turn to another. Solving these whets and sharpens the interest. By this process, through some psychological miracle, the job at hand soon becomes the dominant interest. This interest constitutes the necessary mood which is favorable for a willing imagination.

Having acquired the proper mood and set about the task at hand, the working mood will last for the duration of the job, unless some occurrence arouses a stronger interest in something else. To avoid this, the thinker should insulate his interest in the job at hand from competing interest insofar as possible. Normal activities in the nonworking hours do not, in general, interfere. Anything of importance which arouses a strong, competing interest should be avoided. For many persons, trying to carry on multiple creative projects at one time is like trying to serve several masters. Occasionally, a thinker seems to be able to switch from one project to another and transfer his interest satisfactorily. This, however, may result in many projects started but few finished.

The interest we have indicated as essential to successful creative thinking is precisely the "disturbed state" which is said to be necessary if researchers are to create new ideas and inventions.

Creative thinking requires concentrated attention and so is tiring. When the thinker becomes tired, he should lay aside his creative work. Any further effort will give poor results. He can, however, turn to more routine activities without jeopardizing his interest in the major project.

Interestingly enough, there is an alternate method of generating interest. If a deadline is coming up, the individual becomes more disturbed and agitated as the deadline approaches, and this brings an emotional reaction that is translated into interest. I once knew a house-to-house salesman who made practically no sales in the first half of the month, but his record improved in proportion as the end of the month approached with the accompanying month-end bills.

In industrial research, if management helps to create the disturbed state through deadlines and frequent inquiries about progress, and if the researcher resolutely woos interest in the project, then creative thinking will not be long delayed for want of a proper mood. One hint to research management seems to follow as a corollary. May too much routine work by a trained man stretch his span of interest until it breaks, and thus reduce his creativeness?

Inspiration

Quite different from imagination are the other tools for creative thinking—inspiration and illumination. They are less deliberate and controllable.

Occasionally, a high order of creative activity is induced by what is called *inspiration*. It comes unheralded and without effort on the part of the thinker. Many examples of inspiration have been recorded in various creative fields. Who has not heard of Newton and the falling apple, which is supposed to have inspired him to formulate the theory of gravity?

Several characteristics seem to be common to most cases of inspiration. The experience is very pleasant and stimulating. The idea is totally new and usually unrelated to anything that the individual is doing at the time the inspiration comes. The new idea is sometimes sufficiently detailed to constitute a complete solution to the problem involved. In other cases the inspiration furnishes a complete frame upon which imagination can readily build a finished concept. In all cases the experience automatically creates an abundance of interest which sets the imagination racing, thereby creating strong motivation for completing the project.

The occurrence of inspiration is completely beyond control and it is always unexpected. Nevertheless, the individual must be susceptible to inspiration. This appears to involve two factors. One has to do with the individual's background, study, and experience; the other has to do with the individual's temperament.

A study of the cases of inspiration indicates that engineers may have inspirations about bridges or steam engines, etc., but apparently seldom have inspirations to write music. Musicians, in turn, do not usually have inspirations to paint a picture, nor do painters have inspirations about laws of nature. Inspirations that lead to outstanding contributions come only to those whose minds are properly prepared. This preparation seems to involve stored knowledge and experience in the given field and usually a long history of wrestling with problems related to the field, even though the individual may not have consciously tried to solve the particular problem that is the subject of his inspiration.

Not all individuals are equally susceptible or emotionally tuned for inspiration. It appears that inspiration is, at least in part, associated with action of the subconscious mind. The individual's habitual relationships between conscious and subconscious mental processes probably have an important effect on his susceptibility.

Whatever one's inherent susceptibility, there may be ways in which the individual can woo inspiration. The probability of its occurrence is increased by enlarging the stock of experience and ideas. The painter may seek inspiration by traveling to picturesque or colorful places; the philosopher, by seeking solitude. In many fields, and especially with many individuals, the search for inspiration is a rather barren chase. But, in any case, if hunting for inspiration is usually futile, certainly passively waiting for it always is.

There are individuals that depend on inspiration for their ideas. As such individuals usually are not consistent producers, they often lack the energy and determination to carry projects through to completion. Such a thinker is apt to leave many of his projects unfinished. For sustained creative effort, one needs ample application of the controlled mental processes.

Illumination

Next to imagination, the most important tool for creative thinking is illumination. Like inspiration, it involves a good deal of subconscious activity; but unlike inspiration, it has a certain degree of controllability. An example of illumination will serve as a basis for examining its characteristics.

James Watt is generally credited with inventing the steam engine. Actually, what he did was to make an essential improvement which made the steam engine economically practical. The Newcomen steam engine, which was in use at the time, was operated by alternately filling the cylinder with steam and then cooling it with a jet of water. Thus, air pressure on the piston forced it in one direction and steam forced it back. Watt concluded that this alternate heating and cooling of the heavy cylinder wasted about three-quarters of the heat. He set about to devise a means of avoiding this wasteful procedure.

He wrestled with this problem for two years without a solution. Then, "on a fine Sabbath afternoon" while taking a walk, a solution suggested itself in a manner which Usher[8] has recorded as follows:

> I had entered the green and had passed the old washing house. I was thinking of the engine at the time. I had gone as far as the herd's house when the idea came into my mind that as steam was an elastic body it would rush into a vacuum, and if a connection were made between the cylinder and an exhausting vessel it would rush into it and might then be condensed without cooling the cylinder . . . I had not walked further than the Golf house when the whole thing was arranged in my mind.

---

[8] Abbott Payson Usher, *History of Mechanical Inventions;* Harvard University Press, Cambridge.

From this account we note that Watt had set himself a problem which, after two years of conscious application of imagination and reason, was still unsolved. Then, upon turning his attention to the problem during the enforced idleness of the Sabbath, the solution came to him suddenly and without effort on his part. Moreover, the experience could not be classed as inspiration.

This type of mental creative experience is called *illumination*. It is an experience relatively common to creative thinkers, and the frequent use of it in solving minor problems only seems to make it seem more startling when it brings the solution to a major problem.

Use Illumination

At first thought, illumination appears to be an accidental and uncontrolled experience. In reality, its controllability lies somewhere between that of imagination and inspiration—perhaps, nearer to the former. Illumination is a highly desired product of a mental process which, although it cannot be induced at will, is quite likely to occur if the stage is properly set.

The mental process involved in illumination, like any other process, is controlled by certain natural laws and conditions. By following these laws or rules of conduct, the creative thinker can make effective use of this important creative tool.

Illumination is a problem-solving process that can be invoked only if the following prerequisites are fulfilled:

1) *The problem is a difficult one:*

The thinker must not only have a problem to solve, but the problem must also arouse his active interest. The individual must be motivated to the point of having developed a "disturbed state" about the problem.

2) *The problem has been attacked by intensive thought:*

The thinker must actively apply the conscious processes of logic and imagination in seeking a solution. The problem must be examined from every angle in a sustained effort in trying to get the answer.

3) *The problem has not been solved:*

The deliberate processes of creative thinking must fail in

obtaining a solution. The failure to find a solution is exasperating, but if anything, it intensifies interest in the problem. Something about the make-up of a creative thinker makes his interest increase almost in proportion to the difficulty of the problem.

4) *Interest has been sustained:*

Illumination, no less than imagination, requires the interest of the thinker. In general, once the interest has been aroused, the mere absence of a solution is sufficient to hold the thinker's interest. If conscious attention to the problem is dropped, and if illumination does not bring forward a solution, the interest will dissipate and gradually fade. The greater hazard, however, arises from the fact that interest is a jealous siren who will court only one project at a time. Interest in one problem will surely disappear if a rival project wins the attention. Loss of interest is a certain bar to illumination.

Should this occur, the remedy is to redevelop methodically the interest in the original project. It is, however, better not to have transferred the interest in the first place.

5) *The mind is relaxed:*

The conscious thought processes prevent illumination. Only when the mind is relaxed is the thinker rewarded with solutions from his subconscious mind. The relaxed condition may represent no more than those occasions during the day when the thinker lifts his mind's eye to the horizon and lets his mind wander for a few moments. Other likely occasions are at the close of day when the work is laid aside; as one relaxes just before going to sleep at night; in the morning just after awakening.

6) *The thinker must be relaxed:*

At first thought, one is tempted to say that the mind must not be tired, because illumination does not occur under those conditions when we think of our mind as being fatigued. There is no evidence, however, that the mind does become tired. More likely, the mind becomes inhibited by the emotional tensions that build up during any prolonged struggle with a problem. The usual way to relax these emotional tensions is by sleep. Sometimes they can also be dissipated by a brisk walk, or a fast workout at a gym or in a pool. The requirement for relaxation accounts for the fact that illumination often occurs in the morning before the day's work is started.

Using the Creative Processes

Such are the mental processes that all creative thinkers use to solve problems that do not respond to logic. Such also is the nature of each of these three important processes insofar as they are understood. If these creative tools are used regularly and intelligently, they will yield good returns in creative productivity. Let us now review how they should be used and in what order.

First, it is well to remember that creative thinking is work—constructive and often pleasant to be sure, but nevertheless serious work, requiring intense concentration and lots of perseverance. The individual who does not have such an inquiring mind and a curiosity that beckons him or who does not have the willpower to keep trying after repeated failure, had better content himself with routine-type work. He is lacking in the essential primary requirements for success as a creative thinker. Haphazard thinking will lead to very spotty results.

Now let us trace the steps that are usually taken in the creative thinking involved in the solving of problems. Fortunate is the person that begins on a problem in which he is already interested. If the required project does not already command priority in interest for the researcher, the first step is to build interest. This can be done by consciously solving small problems associated with the project. The author may set about selecting a title; the laboratory researcher might build a bibliography, or design a data sheet.

If no other means of attacking the problem and/or arousing interest occurs to the researcher, he can fall back on the simple but basic procedure of rank-ordering the events or factors of the problem. To do this, characteristic factors are selected that can be quantified, at least in a rough way. These factors are then arranged in descending or ascending order of magnitude. This procedure in itself often brings insight into the problem.

If the noncreative, logical thought processes, including observation, reflection, remembering, reasoning, and judgment, do not resolve the problem, the researcher must turn to creative thinking. To use this effectively, he must be prepared to follow the required rules. This may require a good deal of faith, but experience shows it to be well-placed faith.

The researcher will first turn to imagination in applying the creative thought processes to step 4 (see Chapter 2)—proposing a likely solution or hypothesis. The use of imagination furnishes new combinations from old ideas. In doing this it relies primarily on easily remembered ideas and facts. Adequate attention to steps 2 and 3 supplies the imagination with the broadest possible base from which to build new combinations. Step 3 is especially important, because it brings to mind the pertinent scientific principles, laws, and equations that apply to the problem at hand. Step 3 may be likened to a last-minute review before an examination.

Sometimes the consciously directed and reason-supervised creative process of imagination also fails to solve our problem. If no likely solution has come from these deliberate thought processes, the researcher must next turn to illumination. Fortunately, the steps taken in seeking a solution through deliberate thought processes are the very ones that prepare the thinker to use illumination.

The foregoing should not be taken to indicate that the creative worker should only attempt to apply illumination as a last resort. Consistent and regular use of illumination will reduce the amount of prolonged deliberate thinking required for solving difficult problems. The use of illumination often requires the lapse of two or more days to reach a solution; for, as was pointed out above, the relaxed mind and freedom from emotional tension, which are favorable to illumination, are most likely after a night's sleep. Many individuals unknowingly use this technique. How often have you said or heard others say, "I want to sleep on this"? If the mind is properly prepared, "sleeping on the problem" is an excellent way to use illumination.

The proper preparation is *at least* as important as the sleeping part of the process. As a preparation, the conscious, deliberate thought processes must be diligently applied. The problem should be turned over and over in the mind to consider it from every angle. Then and only then may the thinker hopefully turn to his subconscious processes for assistance. To do this he must consciously and definitely assign the problem to the subconscious for solution. It does not even hurt to assign a deadline for review, although this is unnecessary. A mere stopping of the deliberate thinking about the problem may result in a subsequent solution by illumination, but conscious attempts to use this process should include the definite assignment to the subconscious.

Once the problem has been turned over to the subconscious, the thinker must guard against loss of interest. He must avoid turning his attention to any other exciting problem. Rather, he must busy himself the rest of the day with more routine activities and should bring his attention back to the problem occasionally. Participation in ordinary family and social affairs in the evening do not usually interfere with the chances for illumination. Finally, the individual ought to be in pretty good physical trim. Poor physical tone, such as results from a cold, biliousness, loss of sleep, and dissipation, will not improve the chances for effective creative thinking, conscious or subconscious.

The final step in preparing for illumination is to bring attention back to the problem when the thinker's mind is refreshed and relaxed. This favorable condition is most often found just after arising in the morning and before entering into the work of the day. If the creative thinker does not immediately rush into the affairs of the day, he is prepared to receive illumination with a relaxed, undisturbed mind. I have found the period during a morning bath and shave ideal. Other ways of enjoying undisturbed meditation in the morning include rising well ahead of the rest of the family to garner an hour or so for quiet thinking and study; taking a walk after breakfast (walking to work is excellent if the distance permits); or a long commuting trip to the office can be used for contemplation.

By following these rules the researcher can develop skill in using illumination. It is a very effective tool for problem-solving, and every researcher ought to develop the habit of making regular use of it. But even this effective tool will not bring a solution for every problem. If the first attempt fails, the process must be repeated. The creative thinker must wrestle with the problem again, using the deliberate processes of logic and imagination. He must reexamine the problem from every angle and check to make sure that no pertinent data have been overlooked. If he still has no solution, he will turn again to illumination. A really tough problem may resist solution even after many attempts. It is in such cases that inspiration occasionally comes at some later date with an unexpected solution.

What then is the difference between inspiration and illumination? Probably the mental processes involved are the same for each. Inspiration appears to be even more deep-seated in the subconscious and less controllable than is illumination. Illumination comes when, after suitable preparation and a period of incubation, one sets his relaxed mind to thinking about the problem again. By contrast, inspiration is apt to come when one is giving not the slightest thought to the problem with which the inspiration is concerned. By no known procedure or set of rules can the creative thinker plan to call upon inspiration to aid him with a problem as he can with illumination.

In all probability, inspiration concerns itself with only those tough problems that have proved too refractory for deliberate thinking and for illumination. Such a problem is kept in the active file of the subconscious mind. Eventually, some new facts are received which have a bearing on the problem, or some new combination of old facts results in a solution which the subconscious mind forces out into conscious thought.

BRAINSTORMING

Other techniques in ideation have been developed to make better use of the nature of human thought processes. Some of these concern the individual; others involve the group activity that has come to be known as "brainstorming". There is some doubt whether, in fact, group problem-solving offers any synergism. Some believe that if individuals apply the techniques developed for the group approach to new ideas, the individuals will out-perform the group. It will suffice here to examine these techniques and to note how they can be applied either by an individual or by a group.

Many writers in the field have pointed out that it is not difficult to make new combinations of old ideas; that, in fact, daydreaming and the weaving of fantasies is a widely practiced activity. What is more difficult is to get new and different ideas that are *better*. Only these can really be classed as creative. John Arnold even goes further and qualifies his definition of the creative process by requiring that it lead to some tangible result. He says:

> An idea by itself is not the sum total of the creative process; it is only the beginning. An idea is conceived, it is developed, it is communicated and sold to others before the process of innovation is completed.[9]

Creative mental activity is deeply imbedded in the subconscious, or as some authors call it, the "primary thought processes." The ability to play—that is, to enjoy, to fantasy, to laugh, to be spontaneous—is deeply imbedded in the subconscious, and these activities or abilities are closely associated with creative thinking. These activities are characteristic of children who practice them to the exclusion of judgment and logical thinking. As adults pride themselves on judgment and practicality, they frequently fail to give play to these spontaneous subconscious activities. This represses creativity and in the most controlled individuals may almost preclude it. Studies of creative individuals show that they have sufficient self-confidence to permit themselves to regress temporarily to the spontaneous mental play of childhood. In fact, studies of creativity indicate that highly productive original thinkers easily and regularly shift back and forth from these primary subconscious processes to the secondary, controlled, logical mental processes.

The highly controlled logical individual tends to accept the world as it is and to adjust to it. The creative individual at times rebels at the real world and seeks to escape from it by conjuring up one more to his liking. To the extent that this is done purposefully, he is apt to create ideas for improvements in the environment.

John Arnold points out that ". . . nothing fails like failure and so we avoid making a mistake as we would avoid the plague; it is better to be safe than sorry." [9] It is this fear of failure or of ridicule by one's peers that helps to thwart the

---

9 In *A Source Book for Creative Thinking;* see footnote 1.
9 *Op. Cit.,* page 130; see footnote 1.

use of the primary thought processes and prevents many adults from experimenting with new "wild" ideas. He lists three types of mental blocks that inhibit creativity: *perceptual, cultural,* and *emotional.*

The individual is not likely to be very creative if he has an erroneous conception of the world. Such an individual has a habit of seeing things from one point of view, something like always seeing a map in two dimensions and being blind to the third dimension. The perceptual block is indeed common.

Cultural blocks include all the social pressure for conformity. Creative individuals are found to have a high degree of personal evaluation which gives only secondary consideration to external evaluations. For this reason they are apt to be nonconformists.

PRACTICE CREATIVITY

On the basis of his studies in creativity, Arnold has proposed a ten-point program for personal development:[9]

1) Know yourself as well as possible.
2) Carry a notebook and use it.
3) Ask yourself a new question every day.
4) Develop craftsmanship in your own field.
5) Read and broaden your own interests.
6) Develop creative avocations.
7) Provide permissive atmosphere for family and colleagues.
8) Develop a sense of humor.
9) Speculate and daydream.
10) Question—observe—associate—predict.

If we accept Arnold's specification that a new idea must be useful to be creative, then quite clearly creative thinking involves two factors: 1) new ideas, and 2) evaluation. With most individuals the first step is probably weaker. One of the key ways to increase the number of new ideas relative to a given problem is to separate the idea-generating activity from the judgment stage; as Bill Gordon[10] would say, "postpone closing the loop." If the individual will consciously seek ideas—good, bad, trite, even silly—one idea will lead to another; and through this playing with ideas, some really new and unexpected combinations come to mind. Applying judgment to each

---

[9] *Op. Cit.,* page 138.
[10] W. J. J. Gordon, *Synectics;* Harper & Brothers, New York, 1961.

idea as it arises seems to break the pattern and limit the possibility of generating really new combinations. Several researchers have found that the number of new ideas conceived as an answer to a problem is positively correlated with the uniqueness of the best idea. In other words, the more ideas the individual or the group proposes, the more likely that a really good one will be found.

To prolong the period of ideation and the attitude of play, Gordon proposes some specific techniques. He recommends that the individual seek a feeling on one hand of detachment, and on the other hand of involvement. That he defer accepting any solution, continuing to seek still other and hopefully better ideas. That he let his speculation run free. And finally, that one develop the feeling that the object or process has an autonomy of its own.

To enhance the application of these attitudes as an approach to creativity and problem-solving, he has developed a process that he labels *The Synectic Process*. The steps in this process are designed to help the individual lift himself out of mental ruts and to avoid thinking in circles about a problem. The process involves:

    1) Making the strange familiar;
    2) Making the familiar strange.

The step "making the strange familiar" has to do with stating the problem. The problem obviously is unfamiliar, else its solution would be known. In this stage, looking at the problem from every angle, and especially orienting the problem as a system within a system in relation to other systems, is important. This is precisely what step 1 in the problem-solving procedure of Chapter 2 is supposed to accomplish.

Gordon lists four ways of attempting to make the familiar strange:

    1) Personal analogy;
    2) Direct analogy;
    3) Symbolic analogy;
    4) Fantasy analogy.

Personal analogy involves identifying one's self with the elements of the problem. It consists essentially of asking one's self, "Where would I hide if I were a lost pocketbook?"; or, "How would I feel if I were a hunted fox?"; or, "How would I act if I were a brake shoe?" This kind of conscious transformation frequently works wonders in freeing the individual from a limited perspective of the problem.

Direct analogy consists in comparing the problem with some analogous situation in another field. A common and frequently useful analogy is to relate a mechanical problem to a biological situation. Many of our most effective new detection and guidance systems in the military have developed from observing behavior of insects, snakes, and other biological specimens.

Symbolic analogy differs only in that the analogy is not real; it might be taken from mythology, poetic expression, magic, or any other source where a parallel can be pictured.

Fantasy analogy goes a step further: Here one actually plays at make-believe. He would consciously attempt to push natural law out of phase, invert it, or eliminate it. This might involve a situation where water runs uphill, or where friction does not generate heat.

A part of the whole process of avoiding and postponing "closure" (solution to the problem) includes the use of play and irrelevance. Play in this sense involves the use of illusion, of conscious self-deceit, and of associations in general that seem to imply no immediate benefit. It is clear that this sort of mental activity requires toleration of irrelevance. It takes a fine balance and a good deal of self-discipline to be able to play constructively, to accept irrelevant ideas and yet not wander completely from the problem. This is one of the skills required to develop the ability to generate ideas effectively.

As further assistance in generating ideas, Osborn has developed a checklist which is intended to stimulate viewing the problem from many different perspectives. The list includes:

> Put to other uses
> Adapt
> Modify
> Magnify
> Minify
> Substitute
> Rearrange
> Reverse
> Combine

Fritz Zwicky of Aero-Jet Corporation uses what he calls a *Morphological Chart*,[11] in which he lists different attributes related to a problem on a three-dimensional grid to call attention to many possible combinations.

Up to this point the discussion has examined the individual's potential for creative thinking, how he goes about it, and how he might become more effective at problem-solving. This focuses on the individual, separate and alone. By nature, however, man has the dual characteristic of being both gregarious and individualistic. Although each of us wants freedom to be ourselves, we also want to be with and around others. We want their associations and approval. For the best results in problem-solving we should make use of our social instincts too. Henry James[12] expressed his convictions about the value of group effort as follows:

> The best things come, as a general thing, from the talents that are members of a group; every man works better when he has companions working in the same line, and yielding to the stimulus of suggestion, comparison, emulation. Great things of course have been done by solitary workers; but they have usually been done with double the pains they would have cost if they had been produced in more genial circumstances. The solitary worker loses the profit of example and discussion.

In addition to improving our skill for individual problem-solving, we must also bring into play group attention to our tough problems. There are probably numerous ways of getting assistance on a problem. It will be sufficient to call attention to just two of them.

One way to bring a problem into the social situation is to seek out a colleague and discuss it with him, asking his suggestions or advice. This procedure often proves to be very fruitful. Many times the colleague does not offer anything specific that aids in the solution. The researcher, however, who has to state the problem to the colleague, clearly and completely, often gets new insight as he states the problem or answers the colleague's questions.

Discussing a problem with colleagues is often helpful. In doing this it is wise for the researcher to have done a good

---

11 In *A Source Book for Creative Thinking*, pp. 255-256, see footnote 1.
12 Quoted in *The Management Review*, page 499, September 1953.

deal of spadework first, himself, lest he get into the habit of merely leaning on others.

The other group approach is the "brainstorming" technique, which was introduced by Alex F. Osborn and has been modified by others. By this procedure the active attention of a group is brought to bear upon a problem, with the specific objective of developing new ideas for solving or attacking the problem.

Rules for Brainstorming

Osborn has found that certain rules should be followed to get good participation by a group. At least to start off a new brainstorming group, it is helpful to have a good leader who is skillful at eliminating self-consciousness and encouraging participation. The leader should come to the session with the problem clearly stated and the objective in mind. Through the statement of the problem and by other means, the leader will direct the group to keep a broad perspective and thus avoid narrow, channeled thinking on the problem.

Osborn proposes that there should be no interruptions during a two-hour session, but that the group should not be allowed to become static. Arranging to have one less chair than participants is suggested as a way to introduce desirable movement within the group. When one member gets up to get a drink, empty an ash tray or adjust a window blind, he is likely to be minus a seat until someone else gets up. This informal, undirected game of musical chairs encourages informality and prevents the group from developing a "set" so far as the group relationships are concerned.

Most important of all, there must be no judgments passed upon any idea put forth. In one respect our thinking functions can be divided into two opposites:

1) *Judicial* thinking, which analyzes, compares, chooses;
2) *Creative* thinking, which visualizes, recombines, and generates new ideas.

The first calls for a doubting, suspicious, negative attitude; the second for the faith that underlies a positive attitude. The man that boasts of having both feet on the ground is likely to be short on new ideas. Robley Feland has put it this way: "How far can you walk with both feet on the ground?"

During a brainstorming session not even the suggestion of any evaluation, judgment, or criticism of any idea should be put forth. In actual practice, it often happens that a silly idea breaks the trend of thought and leads to some good, novel ideas. By following these simple rules, any group can come up with novel ideas—perhaps more of them than would the same individuals thinking about the problem alone. According to the proponents of brainstorming, the interaction of the group is the catalyst that brings about this synergistic effect.

The factor of judgment can be added at a later session which devotes itself solely to evaluating all the ideas that were suggested.

This analysis should not lead to the assumption that problem-solving and the creative thinking that it involves is a simple, step-by-step process. This would be, without doubt, oversimplification. As Turner Alfrey[13] puts it:

Many problems are not solved by one fell swoop, but rather by a complex interplay of *partial* preparation, *partial* insight, *partial* verification, gradually converging on the solution.

That this happens often, perhaps usually, cannot be denied. There may be some question, however, whether this needs to happen as often as it does. The reason why the approach to a solution is so often a series of approximations is either because the objective has not been clearly or fully enough stated, or because our first assembly of facts overlooked some pertinent ones. The six-step procedure, outlined in Chapter 2, is specifically designed to minimize the amount of meandering, dead ends, and false starts in seeking a solution. Sometimes, however, even the most careful procedures will not lead to a straight-through solution. It may not be possible to give an adequate statement of objective at the start of the project. The researcher may have to develop some new facts through experimentation before he can determine the scientific field involved. This is why the procedure outlined in Chapter 2 suggests rechecking and reevaluating the objective at various steps as the project develops.

In attacking a problem, the researcher should follow the non-

---

13 Turney Alfrey, *The Psychology of Invention in Chemistry, Physics and Mathematics* (an unpublished lecture).

creative procedures set forth in the first three steps of Chapter 2. He should follow the steps in order:

1. Carefully and fully state the objective.
2. Collect the pertinent data.
3. Arrange the material in an orderly fashion, including determination of the scientific field involved.

These first three steps prepare the researcher for step 4, a proposed solution to the problem—the preparation of a hypothesis relating the facts. This preparation gives a firm basis for attempting a solution by logic. If logic alone fails, the use of logic plus imagination, constitutes just the careful preparation required to make use of illumination. Thus, we see that the steps outlined in Chapter 2 are designed to enhance the use of logic and imagination in seeking solutions to problems. At the same time, the very same procedures multiply the chances for successful use of illumination if the deliberate thought processes fail to give a solution.

chapter 4

TAKE ACTION—
SELL RESULTS

One of the most remarkable research men of our generation used to have a motto hanging in his office which reads:

> FOR EVERYONE WHO DOES SOMETHING,
> TEN OTHERS HAD THE SAME IDEA,
> BUT THEY ONLY THOUGHT ABOUT IT.

This was to remind him and his colleagues that nothing is really accomplished until the idea is put to work. In fact, ideas without plans are idle curiosity, and plans without action is daydreaming. But how does a researcher get action in an industrial, division-of-labor society? Of a certainty, he will have to sell his idea to others. In a commercial setting, the researcher will need to sell his results to the head of his laboratory. The director of research will need to sell the results to his top management. Even the top management will need to sell the results of research if outside financing is needed. The researcher in a university laboratory must also sell his results to his colleagues to earn recognition and to have his results used.

REPORTS ARE IMPORTANT

Effective selling of the results is the key to personal recognition, to rewarding financial return, and even to use of the idea by society. A research finding is valuable in proportion as it is unexpected and radically different from past practice. But the more unusual an idea, the less readily it is accepted, and hence, the harder it is to sell. Sometimes it requires as much ingenuity

91

to sell a research result as was needed to solve the problem in the first place. The most fundamental advances in new concepts often take from one to several generations to gain acceptance.

There are many means for selling the results of research, and the research report is central to them all. It reports the research and the results, and if it is effectively written it will, by itself, do much to enlist interest in and acceptance of the results. After a good research report has been written, attention should be given to such questions as: *who, what, when, where,* and *how.* Who should receive the report? In a large research organization this may be indicated by established policy. A little careful attention, however, may suggest that a copy to some nonregular recipient may get special attention. In publishing research reports, selection of the right journal will increase the effectiveness. Timing may be important. Should you attempt to sell your work late in the day when both you and the "boss" may be tired, or just before a board or budget meeting? Many local and personal factors need to be considered in timing.

One general factor merits consideration. Studies show the minimum of intellectual activity in the northern hemisphere in July and August. This appears to be something more fundamental than the fact that vacations are usually concentrated in the summer months. Perhaps the hot weather and pleasant outdoor conditions divert attention to more primitive pursuits. A peak of enthusiasm and interest for intellectual projects occurs in the early fall. Where feasible, the wise researcher will time his major report accordingly.

Another fundamental factor is the emotional well-being of the researcher himself which may influence how effectively he will sell his results. Studies by Rex B. Hersey[1] of the University of Pennsylvania indicate that many men have a fairly definite emotional cycle of three to four weeks in length. At the peak of the cycle such an individual will be buoyant and optimistic, and in the trough, more pessimistic and less aggressive. Even for the individual that has no such pronounced cycle, there are times when his physical and emotional tone is better than at

---

[1] Rex B. Hersey, Emotional Cycles in Man, *Cycles,* pp. 325-339, November 1954.

others. This should be considered when making a date to sell an idea.

Other considerations include the manner of presenting the report. Should the complete written report be sent by mail or should it be delivered in person? Should a personal, oral presentation be used, including charts and graphs—perhaps as table-sized flip-charts? A complete coverage of these aspects of selling the results of research would involve a full study of sales and advertising psychology. This would demand a large book in itself and it would carry us too far afield. It will be sufficient here to examine some of the important factors in writing a good research report.

Honest Reporting

The researcher has a duty to try to sell his results. He can and should use the best salesmanship of which he is capable. This does not imply, however, that he may shade his results or omit some unfavorable aspects to ensure acceptance by others. The report on any research must, in all respects, be scrupulously honest and objective. The researcher that seeks to stretch the point a little here and there is building for himself real trouble for the future.

Unconscious Bias

It is rare that a researcher consciously falsifies his reports. The greater danger—the ever-present hazard—is that of unconscious slanting. The researcher's interest in the results and his personal involvement in the project makes it hard for him to be really objective. The following discussion of some of the aspects of writing a good report will indicate some ways of overcoming involvement and increasing objectivity.

Objective reporting requires putting down all the facts. Some result should not be omitted merely because it was out of line with the others. Any question about uniformity of conditions can be footnoted. It is equally as important to footnote the fact if the researcher knows of no reason why some of the results fall out of line. This may result from some unknown factor that was not under control, or it may merely result from some unobserved error in technique in one or more of the runs. Of course, it is pointless to clutter a final report with data on partial runs or runs known to be faulty in technique. Naturally, if a deviation in procedure is accidentally introduced in some run and leads to an interesting result, this will be followed by further tests to evaluate it.

Another way to aid objectivity is to state clearly the assumptions on which the premises involved are based. This not only will help the reader grasp the proposition more fully, but will also assist the report writer to view his subject more broadly.

The question of underlying assumptions is especially important in the social sciences where propositions are often examined solely on the basis of logic and without benefit of controlled experimental testing. The number of false propositions that have been accepted in economics and the other social sciences, because no one has bothered to examine the soundness of the premises, is truly amazing. One can never be too careful on this point. The philosopher René Descartes was so concerned about accepting unproved propositions that he sought to build his philosophy from a single premise. He started with the proposition:

Cogito ergo sum
(I think, therefore I am)

Of this, Bertrand Russell commented that Descartes had made not one but two errors: one, the assumption that he thought; and the other, that thinking proved his existence.

An example will illustrate how examining the underlying assumptions can avoid faulty conclusions. In the past several decades, many economists have concerned themselves with the interests of consumers as a class in society. In fact, this concern is so widespread that a whole body of literature about consumers has developed. There is even a move on the part of some influential politicians to have a Secretary of Consumers added to the Cabinet.

Conclusions based on the consumer's interest have been used to support legislation on prices, tariffs, and business taxes. When we examine the arguments, however, we discover that they are based on the assumption that the consumer is one individual and the producer in society is someone else. Actually, except for children and a few drones, everyone is both a producer and a consumer. Whenever the consumer's interest is given consideration, it must be related to his interest in the production process. *On the average,* the consumer's standard of living can be improved only if productivity can be improved or distribution be made more equitable. To excite the consumers to make demands upon the producers—actually on themselves—is the most colossal shell game ever proposed.

Every research report should indicate the uncertainties or limits of error involved both in the propositions and in the research data upon which they are based. With respect to research data, only the research man or others intimately acquainted with the experimental procedure and equipment can evaluate the limits of error. Even where no precise calculations can be made, the probable error should be estimated in a workmanlike manner. As in examining basic assumptions, evaluation of probable errors will help the research man to see the full implications, and in particular, any weaknesses or uncertainty in his conclusions.

Dimensional Analysis

Another procedure that can improve insight for the researcher is to test equations by dimensional analysis (see Chapter 2). This should be done preferably before, but certainly not later than the preparation of the research report. Dimensional analysis will sometimes show errors in an equation or faulty reasoning about its meaning. Some years ago, Dr. Hodges, of the University of Michigan, was discussing an article in which the author had postulated certain physical significance for each of the constants for the Langmuir adsorption equation. Dr. Hodges wrote the equation on the board, studied it for a moment, then commented that the author's postulates could not all be correct because that would involve adding quantities with different dimensions.

It is well known that statistical data, and particularly the presentation of data in charts and graphs, can be manipulated to give a false impression. For example, if data are plotted to show a scale range from only 70 to 80%, omitting all the area from 0 to 70%, it will leave an impression of variation or rate of change that will be out of proportion to the facts. Unless the reader becomes aware of the situation and makes some mental calculations, his impressions concerning the data will be false even though the data themselves are factually stated. This is only one of many ways in which consciously or unconsciously false impressions can be conveyed by the way data are presented.

Make Research Report Communicate

Although the research report should never be a promotion piece, it need not lack color and life. The researcher should make his report interesting enough, readable enough, and well-enough organized to communicate forcefully the essential results of his research. In short, he must use all the good selling techniques that make a report come to life for the reader. Technical writing actually requires higher standards than literary writing, which concerns itself largely with building a mood. The writer of a report must not only incite interest, but he must also convey to the reader the exact meaning intended.

Essentially, a research report is a job of instruction. The researcher is instructing his management or his colleagues in the facts about his research and the implications of his results. Good report writing should follow the steps and the techniques that are required for a good job of instruction.

Instruction Techniques

Experience shows that a good job of instruction involves four steps.[2] These four steps may be outlined as follows:

1) *Prepare the learner:*

>   Put him at ease;
>   Find out what he already knows about the job;
>   Get him interested in learning the job; and
>   Place him in correct position.

2) *Present the operation:*

>   Tell, show, illustrate, and question carefully and patiently;
>   Stress key points; and
>   Instruct clearly, completely, taking up one point at a time.

---

[2] *Training Within Industry* (TWI) program during World War II.

3) *Try-out performance:*

Test him by having him perform the job;

Have him tell and show you, explaining key points; and

Ask questions and correct errors.

4) *Follow up:*

Put him on his own;

Designate to whom he should go for any needed help; and

Check frequently.

How can these steps be applied to writing the research report and how can they be used to ensure a good instruction job? The first step is to *prepare the reader*. This is, of course, the introduction to the report, which covers the scope of the project. This helps to put the reader at ease for it shows him on what to focus his attention. In introducing the project, the writer should consider what the reader may know about project. The introductory paragraphs should be geared to the reader's need.

Title

Even the title is important in setting the stage in the reader's mind. Its importance was dramatized by a speaker at a meeting of the American Chemical Society some years ago. The speaker was Professor James Kendall, then at Columbia University, who had gained international recognition for research on hydrogen ion mobility in gels. When he was introduced, the title of his paper proved to be almost a small paragraph. He began by explaining why he made no apologies for the long title. He told that the previous year he had been invited to speak at Johns Hopkins University. As requested, he sent the title of his speech to the program chairman, who in turn gave good publicity to the forthcoming speech on "Ionic Migration." On the appointed evening a good crowd assembled in the auditorium, but only half were chemists; the others were Greek students.

A little later Professor Kendall was scheduled to speak to the chemists at the University of Minnesota. Once again he forwarded his title for advanced publicity. His subject was the chemistry of rare earths, a closely related group of elements, and for the sake of brevity the title was merely "Rare Earths." Unfortunately, the reporter made a slight slip and reported his topic as a discussion of "Rare Herbs". Professor Kendall said, "I got by that one pretty well. I spent most of the evening talking about Erbium (one of the rare earth elements), and this seemed to satisfy the many horticulturists who came." Yes, even the title can make a difference.

Reader Interest

Getting the reader's interest is vital to a good selling job. The way to ensure his interest is to show that the report is of value to him *personally*. If the results of this report can add to his success in his company connections, can add to his income or his prestige, you will surely have aroused his interest in what is to follow. It is not safe to assume that the reader is an alert chap who will readily see the value of the project. Give him no chance to overlook it. On the other hand, the approach may need to be subtle. Too candid an approach may backfire.

David Phillips, who teaches executives the art of oral communication at the American Management Association's Academy in Saranac, N.Y., points out that a presentation does not really communicate until the listener feels personally involved. He lists seven impelling urges through which interest can be aroused. They are:

1. Self-preservation
2. Desire for money or property
3. Desire for power
4. Desire for reputation
5. Sentiment
6. Affection
7. Taste (love of art, music, drama, etc.)

Placing the learner in the right position means that the writer must try to take the point of view of the reader. He must include or exclude details based on the reader's need rather than on the hours of research and effort which may have been involved. The amount of history and introductory material should be just enough, but no more than enough, to prepare the reader to grasp the main point. Excessive and unessential introductory details reduce the reader's interest.

At this point the writer should make allowance for mental and emotional inertia. There is a natural tendency to resist a completely new idea. An idea will be more readily accepted if it can be shown to be "not a new and radical discovery, but a natural and logical outgrowth of traditional practice." Perhaps it can be shown to be a new, specific application of a well-accepted general principle.

Another aspect of the right position for good learning is matching the approach used in the report to the type of individual that will read it. John Mills, in his book, *The Engineer in Society*,[3] points out that most individuals are basically either S-type or D-type. The S-type individual is one who instinctively first notes the similarity between things, while the D-type just naturally thinks first of the differences. Scientists, philosophers, logicians, and mathematicians are likely to be of the S-type, whereas lawyers, businessmen, politicians, and most women (according to Mills) are likely to be of the D-type. Now it so happens that if one is reporting to an S-type individual, he may report the problem step by step—the approach to it, the experimental procedure, the results, and finally arrive at a conclusion. Such an approach will find the S-type reader receptive. On the other hand, if this type of presentation is used for a D-type individual, his interest will never really be engaged; his mind will wander long before the conclusion is reached. In fact, he will probably lay the report aside without ever reading to the conclusion. For the D-type individual, the very kernel of the result should be presented at the beginning. If this is startling enough or important enough to impress him, he will then stay with the following discussion to learn the "whys" and the "wherefores."

When preparing the research report, the author should give consideration to the type of reader he wishes to reach. If he wants to be sure that the businessman or the lay reader grasps the conclusions, he had better put them first. As a matter of fact, maybe most research reports should be written for the D-type of individual, because although such an approach may irritate the S-type of individual somewhat, he will probably stay with it to learn such details as are reported.

[3] D. Van Nostrand, Princeton, N.J., 1946.

Outlining the Report

When the introduction has carefully prepared the reader, he is ready to proceed to the body of the report. In this section of the report the author tells, shows, and illustrates. He will need some preparation himself before he is ready to write. He should make an outline, which is really a breakdown of his project into a series of steps that the reader can logically follow. It often happens that the story to be told or the job to be taught has two or more parts which cannot be adequately treated in one integrated sequence. The project may be thought of as having two or more dimensions, each of which must be treated separately. When the author of a storybook faces this situation, he first relates the experiences of one set of characters for a given interval of time, and then directs attention to the action of other characters during the same time.

In treating the multidimensional problem, the author must decide which way to slice his problem. Shall he treat it as vertical slices or horizontal layers? In a set of experiments, should the researcher first analyze the influence of changes in concentration or the effect of changes in temperature? Sometimes the order does not make much difference; at other times it may be important. In making the selection, the author should try to put himself in the reader's place to see which approach might be easiest for him. Whatever way the problem is divided for presentation, the author must be careful to use adequate lead-in statements which will give the reader his bearings. At each step the reader must understand the connection between the given part and the rest of the story.

In preparing the outline or breakdown of the project, the researcher should give special attention to key points. These may be variations in procedure which differentiate his project from previous work. In a catalytic reaction, key points might be preparation of the catalyst and possible trace poisons. The key points are the significant details of technique and insight, which would aid the reader to duplicate the work in a safe, sure way.

The whole object of preparing an outline and listing key points is to aid the writer. During the organization of his material, it is quicker and easier to make changes in the order of a skeleton outline than in pages of descriptive writing. The outline orders and unifies the author's thinking about the project.

The key points make up a list of items which the researcher wants to be sure he does not forget to mention. Some persons say that they can do better by writing without an outline. If such a procedure leads to an acceptable result, it probably means that the author has created a workable outline in his head, perhaps more subconsciously than consciously. Although the outline generally leads to greater efficiency in report writing, one should not become a slave to the outline.

During the writing it sometimes becomes evident that a different order of presentation will give smoother transitions. If so, make the change. A good way to test the written report is to read it aloud. This will reveal any lack of continuity or clumsy sentences, and test transitions and clarity better than sight reading. A still better test is to have someone else read the report and note his reactions. If reorganization during the writing is decided upon, this can be done without a lot of intermediate recopying. Merely cut pages at suitable paragraphs or sentences and rearrange as desired.

Language Is Important

A masterful research report represents a genuine literary achievement. The skill for good writing does not come easy. It takes study, attention to techniques, and lots of practice just as in any other activity. Clear thinking and a full understanding of the idea to be stated is a necessary, *but not a sufficient* preparation for good writing.

In recent years a number of good books and essays have illuminated this subject, discussing length of words, length and structure of sentences, and the whole field of semantics. A few are listed below.[4] This is by no means an exhaustive list, but includes some of the more practical and condensed aids.

---

[4] *The Way to Write,* by Rudolf Flesch and A. H. Lass; McGraw-Hill Book Company, 1955.
The Technique of Clear Writing, by Robert Gunning; McGraw-Hill Book Company, 1952.
Communication: Handling Ideas Effectively, by R. I. Johnson, Marie Schalekamp, and L. A. Garrison; McGraw-Hill Book Company, 1956.
The Craft of Composition, by John Ostrom; Henry Holt & Company, 1953.
Style Guide for Chemists, by Louis F. Fieser and Mary Fieser; Reinhold Publishing Corporation, 1960.
The Essentials of a Good Report, by Florence E. Wall; *Journal of Chemical Education,* 24:129-140, March 1947.
Technical Writing, by T. A. Rickard (3rd Ed.); John Wiley and Sons, 1931.

No attempt will be made here to cover this subject in depth, but a few key points should be briefly reviewed. The practice of following simple but basic rules of grammar will greatly improve clarity of expression. To this end use the active voice where possible; use active verbs, concrete nouns, and short words. Multiple syllable words may be excellent and can be used to give a precise connotation; nevertheless, short words tend to enhance clarity. Strive for short sentences with but a single thought. Correct use of the parts of speech will improve clarity, conciseness, and emphasis. Disregard for the rules of grammar leads to dangling modifiers, strings of adjectival nouns, preposition-verbs, and even confusion between prepositions and conjunctions.

By way of example, consider the adjectival noun and how its usage can give an imprecise meaning. Notice that the following sentence seems to have two meanings, and the reader must guess which is correct: "Too much attention cannot be given to research efficiency." At first glance this sentence seems to be concerned with research about efficiency. If it is rewritten to avoid the improper use of research as an adjective, its meaning becomes clear: "Too much attention cannot be given to efficiency in research."

Clearness of writing can be improved by avoiding "woolly" words, and the use of trade jargon. Have you ever been annoyed by the writings of sociologists and welfare workers who persist in using the word "siblings" for children? The selection of the precise synonym for the thought is a great help, for fine shades of meaning can thus be differentiated. The more directly and simply the thought can be expressed, the better.

Mention should also be made of the importance of the reader's probable vocabulary. New or technical words may need to be defined. For a heterogenous readership it may be effective to include as footnotes involved and extensive definitions, development of equations and their explanations. The use of "picture words" can do much to bring a research report to life. Often the right word will really crystallize an idea and carry it to the reader with full meaning. It is worthwhile to make some special effort to try to find such words in putting across the key points in the research project. As the apperceptive background of each individual will be different, many words raise different images for different individuals. Hence, the value of multiple words and phrases to transfer the author's meaning, along with judicious use of similes, metaphors. The use of alliteration will stimulate attention and aid the reader's memory.

Emphasis, which really means proper balance, can make or break a report. The important facts and conclusion must be given the appropriate attention. Part of this may relate to the space allotted to them, but it also involves the location in the report. In a sense, emphasis and conciseness reinforce each other. A wordy report is likely to conceal the important points.

S. B. Seeley[5] reports an example in which, as a result of wordiness, the thought is more concealed than revealed. He quotes a paragraph from *The Nature of Physical Theory*, by Nobel laureate Percy Bridgeman:

> It must not be understood that we are maintaining that as a necessity of thought we must always demand that physical concepts be defined in terms of physical operations; we are merely stating that if by convention we agree to use only those concepts in describing physical situations to which we can give a meaning in terms of physical operations, then we are sure that we shall not have to retract. Other sorts of concept may be applicable, but such always require justification, and we cannot be sure that the justification will be forthcoming until we have made the experiment. The convention that the physical concepts be defined in terms of physical operations is such an obviously useful one that it is coming to be accepted by physicists and demanded tacitly.

Seeley rewrote it in this form:

> I do not say that thinking requires us to define a physical idea in terms of the physical operation that brought it about. I just say that if, where it applies, we limit our definition to this operation we won't have to change it later on. We could use concepts other than operations to define a physical idea. The objection is they must all first be proved by a test. Physicists find this operational definition useful. They like it and even tacitly demand it.

In this he used only 84 words, as compared to 131 words in the original.

---

5 *Chemical & Engineering News*, 42(41):4-5 (1964).

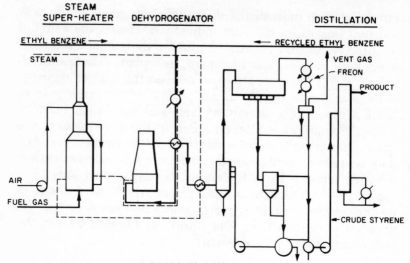

a Usual Flat Diagrams

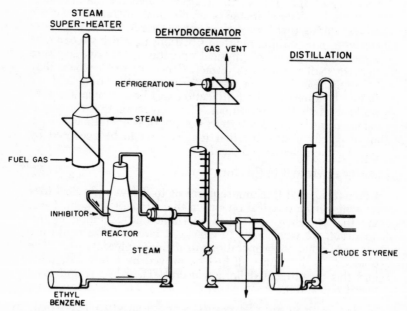

b More Effective Three-dimensional Presentation

Fig. 4:1 PROCESS FLOW DIAGRAMS

Dr. Alan Gregg[6] makes a special plea for clearness and conciseness He says:

> The hallmarks of a good exposition are that it translates or formulates the less familiar into terms that are more familiar; it translates the obscure into the clear, the variant into the constant, the complex into the simple, the vague into the precise, forms into functions, and states into forces.

Illustrations

The *showing* part of presenting the operation covered by a report consists of figures, charts, and graphs. The selection, composition, and location of the charts and graphs in the report should be carefully considered. Where possible, the figures should be in view of the reader as he reads the discussion of the given figure. It is always annoying to have to turn to another page to see the figure. Where feasible, the use of color on charts and graphs will add interest and give a clearer presentation. Even though charts and graphs may fully show the relationships, the author should mention them in the text.

In presenting equations, it is often helpful to point out the effects to be expected from approaching the limits for important variables. This aids the reader in visualizing the scope of the relationships.

In certain types of reports, such as engineering reports on process plants that involve a variety of steps, a three-dimensional pictorial sketch will clarify the relationship of the component parts in the process much more readily than will a two-dimensional line drawing. Figure 4:1 shows the contrast between the two types of presentation.

Great care should be used in preparing charts and graphs to make sure that the labeling and the visual impression quickly convey the essential and true idea involved. One factor here is the selection of the right kind of graph paper: *rectilinear, semi-log, log-log, reciprocal, probability,* or other. Of the many considerations, a few should be noted. *Rectilinear* paper by its nature shows absolute changes; that is, a line, a curve, or a set of data plotted on rectilinear paper leads the reader to notice, primarily, absolute changes in quantities and absolute differ-

---

[6] Alan Gregg, M.D., On the Reading of Medical Literature, *Cycles,* 16 (6):146 (1965).

ences by comparison. *Semilog* paper shows percentage or rate of change, primarily. A straight line on semilog paper shows a constant uniform percentage change. Obviously, if attention is to be centered upon percentage changes or percentage relationships, semilog paper should be used. *Log-log* paper, on the other hand, shows the same type of relationships as does rectilinear paper. It can be used, however, when the span of data is so large that it is awkward to handle on rectilinear paper.

Many other types of graph paper are available and these can be effectively used for special purposes. The more common ones include: *probability* paper, *square-root* paper, *reciprocal* paper, and *triangular coordinate* paper. Mr. Gerald A. Lessells has given an excellent discussion of possible uses of various types of graph paper.[7] In the use of graph paper, avoid bastard scales and figures where the grid is omitted, thus making interpolation difficult.

In report writing, *to illustrate* means to give examples. If examples are to be given, they should be chosen if possible to include the experience of the reader. They will not illuminate the problem for him unless the example is something with which he is well acquainted. In selecting examples, it is well to use those that so vividly bring out the point that it tends to stick in the reader's memory.

Recheck

Finally, the report is written; but the first draft should not be thought of as a finished product. You should now carefully and objectively study it in order to revise and polish it. Rechecking involves careful attention to details. Are all relevant data—and only the relevant data—included? Are the formulae correct, and the figures and graphs appropriately labeled? Have you checked the nomenclature, spelling, punctuation, and grammar, including agreement in number, person, and tense? And finally, does the report discuss the subject clearly; does it come to the point quickly, and keep to it? Is the material logically presented? Reading the report aloud is a good way to check it for coherence and to locate any awkward sen-

---

[7] Unusual Graph Papers and Their Uses, *Chemical Engineering*, pp. 141-146, August 11, 1958.

tences. Rereading the report after a lapse of time gives a fresh perspective. If the interval is long enough, the author will have much the same reaction as other readers. He will be able to detect errors that escaped him before, and he can better evaluate the clarity of presentation.

Follow-Through

Steps 3 and 4 of our standard method of instruction are not quite so obvious in report writing as in instructing someone to do a mechanical job. In a mechanical job, it is easy to have him go through the operation, explain each step as he does it, and it is easy enough to check back with him later to see if he is doing it correctly. Although these steps may not seem obvious when presenting ideas, they are nevertheless important if the objective is to get the ideas used. Somehow the report or the follow-up must result in action on the part of the reader, or at least in acceptance of the idea, otherwise little has been accomplished. A skillful selling of the results of the research will go farther than the mere writing of a good report. It may involve personally going over the report with one or more key individuals. It may involve an invitation for questions to clear up any doubtful points. It very probably will involve follow-up to make sure the project is not forgotten.

If the objective of the research report is to induce management to build a plant, or to authorize a pilot plant, either the report itself or the follow-up will need to outline the plan for a proposed action. This plan will need to be complete enough and include enough economic data to permit a financial evaluation.

Much has been written and said about the value of research and the importance of new ideas to society. All of this is true only if the final step is taken, if the research is *sold*. Both the personal and the social rewards from new ideas and inventions come only with the action stage. This is one of the factors in effective research about which the researcher *can* do something. He can equip himself to do the very best possible job of presenting and selling his results.

chapter 5

TRAINING
THE RESEARCHER

The training of the researcher has a lot to do with his efficiency and the value of the results he will obtain. This is another of the factors about which the research man himself can do something. Training refers here not only to his formal education but also to all of the continuing study and self-improvement throughout a lifetime. Attention will be more especially directed to post-school training, because there is so little discussion on this aspect of research. Moreover, even casual observation shows wide variation both in the amount and in the type of continued study by different individuals.

Consider the chemical engineer who became a production supervisor, and who, year in and year out, spent several nights a week and most weekends playing bridge. Now bridge is a fine game; but as for our chemical engineer, it is no surprise that he became a better-than-average bridge player but did not advance professionally. Had he spent some of those many hours in directed self-improvement, he would have been more valuable in his profession. In fact, few, if any, advance to outstanding positions in research or any other endeavor who have not spent long years of continued study and learning.

SCHOOLING

It is possible, even probable, that at an early age some individuals have some experience or training, either formal or informal, that sows the seed that grows into an aptitude for research. It may be that inheritance is a big factor in aptitude for research. In any case, a lot of training is required to develop whatever latent talent a youngster may have. For best results the school program, from kindergarten on, must develop good habits of work and concentration, and at the same time intensify curiosity and creativity. This is no easy requirement, especially because there is considerable doubt about just how the objective is best met.

The decline in the percentage of our college students that elect courses in science and engineering indicates that somewhere we may have made a wrong turn. If there is a national problem of too few scientists in training, the problem had better be attacked in our grade schools. Any program that starts with the high schools can have only partial success.

In spite of the hazards, some college students do take science courses. These are the researchers of tomorrow. What courses should the would-be researcher take in college? Should he take primarily science courses or should he select a broad spectrum of subjects? The latter idea has found a following among a number of business leaders in the past decade. Quite likely, however, they are thinking more about future executives than research men.

College Courses

Even for the researcher, a broad literary background would be a nice addition to his fund of knowledge, but time is the troublesome variable. The young scientist may have to be satisfied to postpone most of the classics for reading during vacation as there are so many "must" courses. First of all, the scientist must prepare himself as broadly as possible in his own field. A chemist would want as many courses as he could include in organic, in inorganic, in physical chemistry, and in quantitative analysis. In like manner, the physicist, the biologist, the medical scientist, the psychologist, the economist, the engineer—all need broad training in the given field.

In addition to all this, there are many other "must" subjects. There are, for example, subjects that can be considered as tools for research. Mathematics is the most important of these. No one should plan to enter *any* field of science without training in mathematics, at least through calculus, and preferably differential and empirical equations. Statistics is rapidly becoming a "must" also. A sound mathematical training is as important for the sociologist or economist as for the physicist. Another important study is thermodynamics. Energy relations, equilibrium, and driving forces are vital to the study of any process, be it chemical, economic, or psychological. All physical scientists need a course in electrical measurements and in heat transfer. And who can doubt the importance of atomic structure and nuclear reaction these days? Every social scientist should have had a rigorous course in logic.

As scientists live and work in society, another "must" is training in the communication skills. Courses in English composition and report writing should be included. Training in public speaking is a valuable addition. Some suggest adding psychology to the list so the researcher will better understand himself, his thought processes, and his fellow men with whom he must work.

Research Method

Finally, one important point should be mentioned. Every young scientist should be taught how to do research. This consists in being taught how to apply the scientific method. Too many colleges have been content to teach the students how to use the separate tools of the trade without taking the next step and indicating in what order to use which tools. Chapters 2 and 3 of this book are designed to show clearly how to apply the scientific method.

It is easy to see that the would-be scientist should have a good start in high school if he expects to complete even most of the courses which he should have. For the practicing scientist whose training is weak in some of the auxiliary fields, the situation can always be remedied. As the old saying goes, "You can't learn any younger."

CONTINUING EDUCATION

Training in college, even through an advanced degree, will not suffice to educate a man nor will it produce a finished researcher. College is only a good beginning, and it should be supplemented by continued study. It is truly amazing how much can be accomplished by a few minutes a day over a period of years. The young researcher should set for himself a threefold objective. He should extend his studies in his own field and keep up to date on the new things; he should enlarge his knowledge in related fields; and he should improve his techniques in research.

There appears to be unanimous agreement that a well-stocked store of knowledge is one of the important factors in creativity. As so aptly stated by Hengstebeck and Sanders[1]:

> Seldom are new ideas sudden inspirations; rather, they result from rubbing old ideas together until a flame is generated. The broader the background, the greater the chance that a flame will be kindled.

Unfortunately, there is no easy way to fill the mind with knowledge. It must be done the hard way. It takes unending study. Happy indeed is the individual that has a real thirst for knowledge. Most of us, however, can find enough family and social obligations of high priority to take all our spare time. To cope with this, it may be necessary to budget some time for study on certain nights of the week, or perhaps early in the morning. Directed continued study is as important as is a savings program. In fact, the two have much in common: by study and reading we store facts and concepts to be drawn upon in the future.

Other Fields of Science

In the study program it is important to include adjacent fields. More often than not, the frontiers of knowledge are advanced in the no-man's land between two fields of knowledge. Sometimes an idea that has proven fruitful in one field can, with suitable adaptation, be applied in another field. During the process of adaptation, new insight may show that the first idea was merely a special case of a more general principle. For example, broader application of Newton's *First Law of Motion* gave a lead for the concept of reversible equilibrium chemical reactions, and ultimately led to Henri Le Chatelier's Principle, which states:

---

[1] R. J. Hengstebeck and W. W. Sanders: Appraising projects for research, *Chem. Eng. News,* page 85, August 11, 1958.

The equilibrium of the system when displaced by a stress, is displaced in such a way as to tend to relieve the stress.[2]

In a more modern vein, we might remind ourselves of the implication for social scientists of the *Heisenberg Uncertainty Principle* in atomic physics. This is the aggravating problem of the effect of the measurement on the subject. Anyone that hopes to make important discoveries should develop a comprehensive view or way of looking at the world around him.

The scientific genius is an individual that at some stage, probably unconsciously, developed a good approach to problem-solving and to research. Most researchers, however—either less fortunate or less gifted—can improve their efficiency by conscious attention to methods. The first step is to get a clear mental picture of the steps and sequence in the scientific method. The next is to gain practice in the application. From time to time the young researcher should examine his procedures; ask himself how he could have done the recent project more quickly and efficiently. Thus, by systematically studying and improving his procedures, he will develop a good technique in research which will benefit him year after year.

Curiosity

Few will have selected science as a career that do not have more-than-average inquisitiveness. This is a valuable trait, and it should be consciously developed. The young scientist should train himself until inquisitiveness and doubt are automatic reactions. He will want an inquiring, seeking mind, balanced by healthy doubts about the adequacy of any explanation or theory, or the statement of any natural law. In a sense, he should never outgrow his childhood, at least as far as questions are concerned. He will then be able to say with Kipling:

> I have six honest serving men,
>   They taught me all I ever knew,
>   Their names are *what*, and *where*, and *when*,
>   And *why*, and *how*, and *who*.

One of the reasons why children are so free with questions is that they have no false modesty; they know that they are not

---

[2] George Sarton, *History of Science*, p. 343; Harvard University Press, Cambridge, Mass., 1952.

supposed to know the answers. We adults resist questions for two reasons. We dislike to ask too many questions about facts lest others get the impression that we are not so smart as they had thought. Similarly, we hesitate to question too much the accepted ideas, theories, practices, and attitudes that are current. We all desire to be accepted by those around us. If we question too much, they may cease to accept us and may begin to label us "queer". There are indeed strong social pressures for conformity. The true scientist must have enough independence and self-reliance to rise above this pressure. One step in this direction is the realization that other people do not pay nearly as much attention to us as we sometimes imagine. Our ego gives us an exaggerated impression of our impact on others.

Human Relations

Mention should be made of one more skill that the researcher should develop, especially if he plans to enter industrial research. In large research organizations the team approach is widely used. Any researcher that would multiply his own effectiveness and value should learn to be a good group discussion leader. He should know how to encourage participation and contribution by all in the group. He will want to be able to create the kind of atmosphere in a group discussion that is conducive to constructive creative thinking and suggestions. One way to gain experience in leading group discussions is to accept chairmanships of community projects and use such sessions as a laboratory for trying out techniques that can be learned by study. One good book for discussion leaders is *Manual for Discussion Leaders*,[3] by Mortimer J. Adler. Another is *Techniques of Conference Leadership*, Studies in Personnel Policy, No. 77, National Industrial Conference Board, New York.

Up to this point attention has been focused on the ways in which the individual researcher can improve his own efficiency. He can improve his training, his report writing, and his method of attacking problems.

A good research director can and will develop an environ-

---

[3] This manual was designed for use in the *Great Books* discussion groups; University of Chicago Bookstore, 5802 Ellis Ave., Chicago, Illinois.

ment that will encourage the individual to strive for self-improvement. He will encourage seminars, evening courses, and individual study. He might, for example, have a seminar for problem-solving, using the method presented in Chapter 2. Nevertheless, the researcher that wishes and expects to advance in efficiency, and hence in value and income, must take full responsibility and initiative for his own program of self-improvement and continuing education.

chapter 6

SELECTING THE PROBLEM

As indicated in Chapter 1, the factors that determine efficiency in research can be divided into two classes: Those that are primarily the responsibility of the researcher himself; and those that are primarily the responsibility of management. The lone researcher is, of course, his own management.

Problem Is Important

Of the factors for which management is responsible, *selecting the problem* merits first attention because of its vital influence on results. The choice of the research project pre-sets the odds for or against financial success. The other factors—organization, communications, morale, and equipment—play their part, but will profit nothing unless applied to a worthwhile project. The selection of a good project gives leverage to efficiency in all the other factors.

The prime importance of selecting the right problem applies as much to the individual doing the research in the laboratory as to research management or the company or organization supporting the research. In industry, the right problem is one for which the solution yields handsome profits. The importance of this to the company is obvious. In proportion, as the solution proves profitable to the company, the research management and also the man that works out the solution will attain recognition and enhanced future opportunities. The right research problem is so important that the choice of it, or at least the authorization for it, stems from the highest counsels in management. To be a good problem for a particular company, it must harmonize with the organization's economics and philosophy.

This is why it is often wise to include the director of research in the company management and even as a member of the board of directors.

Selecting the right problem is equally important to the academic man working on fundamental research. For him, the right problem is one that is ripe for solution and which will command the attention and recognition of his colleagues. Whether his objective is merely to advance fundamental knowledge or to enhance his reputation and standing among his colleagues makes no difference. Whatever his objective, the attainment of it will be influenced by the problem he chooses to attack.

A little reflection on the nature of problem-solving will indicate the soundness of giving early attention to the selection of the problem. The same steps are required to solve all problems, although the big problems may be more complicated. This often means, however, merely working at different levels of detail. Very often the amount of nervous or mental energy required to solve a trivial problem may not differ too much from that required for an important, worthwhile problem, the main difference being that some problems will never pay their way, whereas the right problem, if and when solved, leads to outstanding profits and growth. Good, well-selected problems will lead to more dollars returned per dollar of research.

What do we mean by a big problem or a trivial problem? By what criteria may one determine that a problem is worth the effort, or fits into the organization's economics? First of all, a good problem is one whose solution fills an important human need. This may be a new device or tool; it may be a better material or a simpler, cheaper process for making a known and important material.

By way of example, let us consider the alternative of doing research on a water-based paint for house exteriors or an improved synthetic perfume. It is obvious that solution of both these problems would solve a human need. From a dollars-and-cents point of view, however, the market for exterior house paints greatly exceeds the market for perfume, and as surely the rewards will be proportionately greater. There are many correlated factors that must be considered. The size of the research staff and budget is one such factor. For example, a lone researcher might make an important contribution in synthetic perfumes, but would meet with formidable obstacles in trying to develop and commercialize an exterior latex paint.

Criteria for Selecting Problem

In selecting a project or problem, first attention should be given to the field in which the project lies. The objective is to find a project which will greatly increase the economic efficiency in some sector of the economy. The rewards for the solution of a problem will be in proportion to the increase in efficiency that results. The odds favor finding pay-dirt in a fast growing field.

In seeking fundamental improvements, it is well to think of function, not method. The key question to be asked is, "What function is to be performed; what service is to be rendered?", rather than directing primary attention to method. If the function can be clearly stated and fully understood, it may become clear that many methods will give the desired result. This may, indeed, help the individual to solve the problem with an entirely new method, and this is precisely the way in which major contributions to increasing efficiency usually are made. In Chapter 2, under *Stating the Objective,* it was proposed that the researcher have an over-all general objective and a more immediate secondary objective. The purpose of the over-all general objective is to help him take a broader look, focus his attention more particularly on the function or service to be performed, and thus avoid a narrow approach. It is even more important to take a broad-gauge approach and consider fundamentals in selecting the problem than in solving it.

In recent years the auto industry has furnished a fine example of the effects of selecting a problem. In seeking more horsepower and greater efficiency in the design of internal-combustion engines, several approaches have been made. One set of engineers focused their attention upon solving the knock problem in high-compression, reciprocating gasoline engines. They turned their attention primarily to the improvement of fuel by use of additives. Other engineers looked at the problem more broadly, and by giving consideration to the mechanics of the

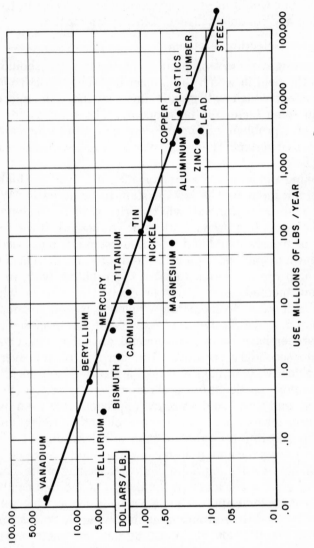

Fig. 6:1 Relation of Selling Price to Volume of Sales

fuel-engine system, designed engines (the Texaco Engine) which would not knock on ordinary fuels even at high-compression ratios. Still other engineers leapfrogged the refinements on the reciprocating engine and focused their attention on the gas turbine. Should the gas turbine become the preferred power plant for the automobile, the truck, and the locomotive, those engineers that focused their attention on the basic function of converting the expansion forces of heated gas to rotational motion and chose a new method for this, will reap more lasting rewards for the research dollars spent.

The genius of the free-enterprise economy lies in the fact that the market price is such an excellent index of the degree to which a given product meets a human need. In general, the lower the price the larger the market. Hence, in a perfectly general way one can say that, other things being equal, the lower cost product is the one to work on, at least if growth is an objective. Low price here refers to ultimate low price, not the price of a development material as compared with established products. Stated differently, it refers to a low price relative to competing products when compared at the same level of development.

There are some products where glamor or snob appeal, is more important than anything else. But, in general, these are for the specialty operator and are not a sound market on which to base an enduring business enterprise. A product that has glamor or snob appeal today may lose it tomorrow. The research manager may best leave this field to the Advertising Department and base his decisions on more fundamental contributions.

Price/Volume Relations

So fundamental is the desire for getting the most for one's dollar that there is a very direct correlation between the selling price of most major products and the volume of their sales. Figure 6:1 shows price/volume relationships for many important solids. It is a bit surprising to discover that there is substantially a straight-line relationship between the amount used and the unit selling price for common metals, wood, plastics, etc., covering a range in volume from 10,000 lb a year, up to steel with a consumption of more than 200 billion lb a year. The straight line as drawn here is not drawn as an average, but rather as a sort of limit in free competitive markets. The same sort of curve, with only a slightly different slope, holds true for chemicals, for plastics, for textile fibers, and in fact, probably for any family of products for which one can isolate a common competitive market.

These curves show that every major product is in competition with many other products for the consumer's dollar. From time to time there may appear temporary circumstances in which a particular product will for a while command a price well above that indicated by such price/volume charts. This situation usually is temporary, however. For example, during World War II, the price for acrylate plastics was so high relative to their volume that they were well out of line with the prices for all other plastics. This was because of the abnormal demand for the acrylic sheet for "blisters" on the noses of bombers and fighter planes. Immediately after the war, both the price and volume of acrylate plastics dropped considerably. In a peacetime competitive market, the price/volume relationship fell into line with those for other plastics.

Low Price a Valuable Property

If research management is looking for growth and good profits, attention must be given to developing products that can be sold at a low price. Here the volume can and usually will be large. A moderate profit on an item of large tonnage leads to handsome rewards for the research efforts. The nice thing about developing low-cost products is that research people in all possible consumer industries will be seeking ways to use the low-cost product in preference to the higher priced product of some competitor. As a matter of fact, it is reported of the Union Carbide Corporation that for years they operated on the philosophy that they would develop a low-cost chemical, make it available, and others would find uses for the chemical. The growth of Union Carbide is ample justification for the soundness of their approach. From the early days of The Dow Chemical Company, the attention in research was focused on making low-cost products that could be mass-produced. This led to mass markets and it was one of the key factors in the past growth of The Dow Chemical Company.

In selecting the product and in thinking about improving general efficiency, the selling price is an excellent criterion. The selling price is primarily a summation of all the costs involved in producing the economic utilities embodied in the given article. Included are all the costs in labor and in capital, and all the wages of entrepreneurial effort. If the selling price is or will be lower than that of competing products, this is a pretty good indication that the new product contributes greater economic efficiency.

Although selling price and costs of production are generally a good guide to true economic costs, they are not always infallible. Accounting procedures do not always credit costs where they belong. Moreover, current market price may be distorted by a transient fad. For this reason the wise research director, after considering the dollars-and-cents factors as best he can, will also attempt other methods of comparison and evaluation. What is needed is an approach like the use of thermodynamics to evaluate mechanical and chemical operations. A step in this direction can be made by matching equivalent parts or steps in two or more methods of satisfying a human need and thereby focusing attention on the really different factors.

Moreover, although dollar profits are at one and the same time the incentive and reward for successful research, it may be unwise to fix the attention too directly on this objective. A good deal of evidence indicates that for the founders of many successful businesses of the past and present, the dollar motive was not the primary driving force. Their basic philosophy and urge was to do an important job better—to improve economic efficiency. Not that the founder was unmindful of profits, but that the production or merchandising idea on which the business was founded held central interest. The dollar profits were truly a reward, a sort of byproduct. In like manner, the astute research director will be concerned primarily with judgments about fundamental economic efficiency, rather than with profits as such. Money will be for him truly a measuring device rather than an end in itself.

This question of economic efficiency takes us directly to the basic economic problem; namely, the problem of supplying man's limitless wants from resources and products that are limited. By nature man is active, not passive; but in satisfying his wants he prefers to do it with the least effort, even though having satisfied one want he merely turns his attention to a new one. Man is expansive about his objectives, but having fixed on any particular one he seeks to minimize the effort required to attain it. In a most fundamental way, service to mankind consists merely in satisfying human needs and wants more effectively. He that successfully dedicates himself to service in this manner can collect a rewarding profit.

TIMING

Is the Project Timely?

The previous section developed the desirability of selecting a field with a good potential growth. An important part of selecting a suitable field is timing. If a company or academic researcher enters a field too early, it will lead to frustration because supporting technology lags.

Rockets are an excellent example of such a case. The Chinese have applied the reaction principle, using solid fuel, for a thousand years or more, but only now has the development of materials, technology, and control mechanisms given the rocket practical significance. Leonardo da Vinci understood the principles of heavier-than-air flight. He also designed a machine gun and other devices which became practical only after hundreds of years of technical and metallurgic development.

The return on research will be disappointingly low if work is done in a field too soon. When an idea or project is too advanced for the times, the researcher must spend too much time developing the supporting technology and the necessary tools for the research. This unduly delays practical results. The leverage involved in the law of compound interest places a high premium on shortening the time between the spending of dollars for research and development and the return of the capital through sales and profits.

By contrast, an entry into a field too late reduces the potential for worthwhile discovery and faces intense competition from those already in the field. In selecting a problem, the wise researcher will avoid such potentially low prospects. Like most generalizations, this one must be applied with judgment. In fact, if a field of technology has been old without showing significant advance for a long time, say fifty or one hundred years, it may be ripe for a giant stride forward. Advances in general technology, materials, etc., may make feasible radically new and better processes. As such an old industry is apt to be large, a small percentage of improvement will mean substantial improvement in the sum of economic efficiency, and consequently will yield handsome profits.

Examination of old established fields or processes may reveal a historical approach and bias which results, in part at least, from an emotional commitment and prejudice—"it has always been done this way." In such a situation, it is likely that important basic factors have been overlooked. If so, then logical, fundamental analysis of the situation may show the possibility for a greatly improved approach to solving the particular human need.

How, then, is the researcher to know when the time is ripe? What clues can he hope to find? It may be that those most successful in solving the problem of timing use a lot of intuition and, no doubt, sometimes are gifted with luck. Nevertheless, there are some fundamental approaches that can be used. One of these is to take note of the most rapidly developing branch or aspect of technology. Dr. Roland P. Soule, of the Irving Trust Company, has pointed out a number of periods during which a particular branch of technology was predominant. He lists[1] them as:

1860-1880	Civil engineering
1880-1900	Electrical engineering
1900-1920	Mechanical engineering
1920-1940	Chemical engineering
1940-1960	Electronic engineering

This latter period was built on the "breakthrough" in solid-state physics. If this period follows the pattern of a 20-year

[1] *Chem. Eng. News,* 39(33):100 (1961).

period as listed by Soule for the others, we can expect to find some other breakthrough dominating the 1960s and 1970s. In any case, the wise researcher will hunt in the newer, more promising, field if he desires superior gains from his efforts in research.

Logistic Curve

Another approach is to consider the growth trend and potential for the industry and for the sector of the industry involved. Studies show that the history of the growth of most products

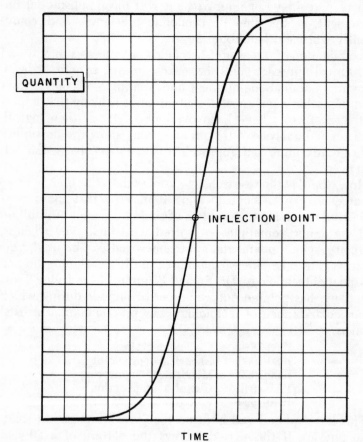

TIME

Fig. 6:2 Logistic Trend: Ordinary Graph Paper

and industries approximate an S-shaped curve, when plotted on ordinary (rectilinear coordinate) graph paper.

Figure 6:2 shows such an idealized curve, known as a *logistic curve.* It will be noted that the curve starts out with a very low slope and then progressively sweeps up from the abscissa until the slope becomes relatively steep. At some point the growth factors weaken and the rate of increase begins to diminish. This is the *inflection point,* and in a curve of symmetrical growth it would be at the halfway point of maximum growth.

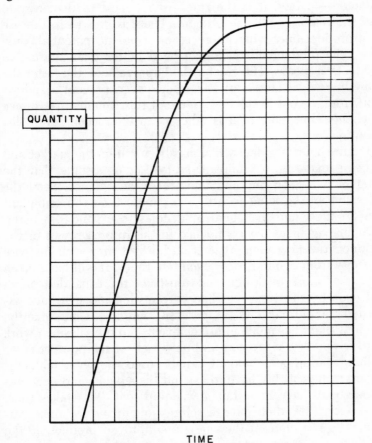

TIME

Fig. 6:3 LOGISTIC TREND: SEMI-LOG PAPER

The same data when plotted on semilogarithmic coordinates give approximately a straight line in the first third or more of the growth, so the slope indicates a uniform rate of growth; see Figure 6:3. If the growth of the field or product has progressed far enough to establish the growth trend, much can be determined about the fundamental factors underlying the growth.

The reader may wonder whether there is, in fact, such an orderly growth for more than an occasional product; and if so, why? That a sustained uniform average rate of growth is common—in fact, it is the rule—is not hard to demonstrate and the reason is not too obscure. There is growth in the use of a product only when there is an economic potential, only when the product fills a human need better than alternative products or means. The greater the improvement, the faster the growth. Several factors of inertia, however, prevent a sudden shift from the old to the new. Some of this is human resistance to change, but more of it is inherent in the mechanics of distribution.

Picture a new product which has been put on the market and is being made on a semiplant scale. Let us assume that the product is a good one and finds ready acceptance. Soon the salesmen are bringing in orders for more than the semiplant can produce, and management decides to expand the plant.

As management has confidence in the future growth of the product, the new plant that is authorized may well increase capacity from two to five, or even ten, times. It will have taken a year or more to design and construct the expanded plant, but even by this time the then current demand will have exceeded the old capacity by, perhaps, only 20%. Consequently, the new plant has much unused capacity, so the salesmen work hard to find new customers and new uses for the product.

Before additional product can be used, however, old customers will probably have to expand their plants and new customers may have to install new equipment. This takes time. Moreover, they then have a selling job to induce their customers to use more of their new or improved product. If the product is a basic material, it may require the expansion of capacity through several successive stages of manufacture.

Conversely, for consumer goods, expansion of the supply all the way back to raw material may involve several stages.

All of these intricate interrelations in marketing represent the resistance to rapid change. The increase in economic efficiency is the driving force. The resultant rate of growth may be thought of as the economic equivalent of current flowing in an electrical circuit with a given voltage and a given resistance.

The use of a good new product grows year by year. At first, the annual increase in growth is likely to average a constant percentage. Later, the *rate* of increase begins to decrease and in old age reaches or approaches zero. The actual growth, month by month or even year by year, will deviate from a smooth curve but it often averages out to a uniform rate of growth over a long period of years.[2]

Let us now examine the forces of economic growth and see what measurements of them can be made. In the normal progress of social and economic development, at some stage a few forward thinkers begin to realize the existence of some specific problem and they begin to seek solutions. The first step in progress is the realization of a problem, and the stating of the problem.

Once the problem has been isolated, it is attacked by creative individuals; and when the contest is engaged, these researchers seek diligently for a good solution. They apply ingenuity and creativity, the highest order of socio-economic energy. A good solution consists in finding a new process or product that increases economic efficiency. This may consist in cost reduction or improved utility. In proportion, as the new process or product increases efficiency, it will begin to take over the market and grow in use. The basic new concept, theory, or invention is the all-important spark which ignites the flame of progress. Without it we would remain in the darkness of stagnation. Even after the spark has been struck, there usually remains the jobs of polishing the chimney and trimming and adjusting the wick to make the light work properly. The development work which makes the new idea practical is

---

[2] See *Growth Trends*, National Industrial Conference Board.

an important part of progress, although applied at a lower level of energy than is the original creativity.

As the development work progresses, the product begins to earn commercial acceptance and the market grows. Soon the increase in economic efficiency begins to pay dividends in the form of profits. The profits justify the confidence of management and further expansion.

What the research director would like to know is: What is the increase in economic efficiency of a new idea? What is its profit potential? Management would also like to know this at an early date, and in addition, would like to know just how valuable is a really creative man. Unfortunately, these questions cannot usually be answered by a simple calculation at the time the new idea is conceived. In fact, even historically, the best calculation may well be indirect.

One useful answer to the question can be obtained by study of the growth-trend curve. As soon as the rate of growth for the product or field can be established, analysis of the data will give a basis for some fundamental judgments. The logistic curve shows the cumulative sum of economic value added, assuming of course that accounting results closely approximate the real values. It is integrated over time and each year adds the new growth to all the previous increments of growth.

By subtracting from any given year the value for the preceding year, one can get the first differences or acceleration of the logistic or growth curve. To the mathematician, this is the first derivative of the logistic curve. From this rate of growth the researcher can apply an important generalization.

Other things being equal, fields or products with the fastest rate of growth will have the best potential. This follows precisely because the economic contribution is large, and technology and markets are ready for the new product or process, or it would not start to grow quickly.

The research administrator will think of this first derivative as the rate of increase or acceleration in the addition of economic value, and will note that it indicates the potential profit. There may be special factors that will prevent the potential profit from being realized, but these are often temporary and will usually yield to longer-term, more fundamental, economic forces.

The first derivative gives some information. In like manner, the second and third derivatives give additional insight into fundamental economic forces and relationships. The second derivative represents the driving force—the increment of economic advantage of the new product or process. It represents the difference in profit from substituting the new and better for the old. The second derivative will remain positive for an industry that is growing faster than the national average, or for a company that sustains a growth faster than that of its industry. In dollars and cents, this says that an industry or company that is truly growing will show a return on investment in excess of average. This tells the research director that the faster the rate of growth, the greater the advantage in potential profit for the given product over alternative use of time and capital. This assumes, of course, equally astute business management.

If the second derivative is considered as the driving force, then the third derivative can be likened to a detonator—the potential, the idea, creativity. This represents the leaven that starts the whole fermentation, the spark that sets the organization on fire. The first two derivatives may be considered as physical in nature and these are measured quite naturally in quantities or dollars. The third derivative, by contrast, involves ideas.

Figure 6:4 shows an idealized logistic curve and its family of derivatives. The scales of each successive derivative have been increased by progressively larger multipliers so as to picture the relationship of the maxima, intercepts, and inflection points of the several curves. It is significant to note that the maximum of the third derivative, i.e., the period of maximum development of the underlying idea, comes fairly early in the growth history. A corollary is that, except as subsequent events change the environment, the future is pretty well indicated by the force of potential relationships in these formative years.

Figure 6:5 is an attempt to show the family of derivatives in quantitative perspective. This family of curves assumes a product that is growing at 15% a year, compounded, during the early history of its growth.

This is a rather rapid acceleration for any major product,

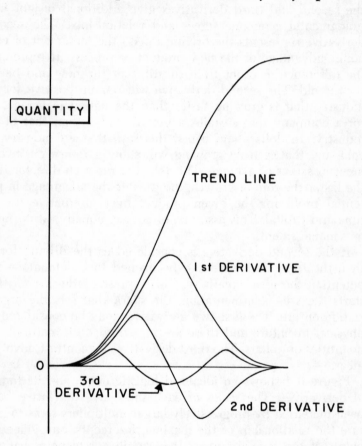

Fig. 6:4 IDEALIZED LOGISTIC CURVE AND DERIVATIVES

company, or industry. Nevertheless, the divergence between each curve and the next higher derivative is most striking. The relative order of magnitude indicates the leverage involved.

The Value of an Idea

Philosophers through the ages have tried to impress us with the power of an idea. The relation between the S-shaped logistic curve and its third derivative gives a mathematical indication of the leverage of the creative idea on future growth and profits. Thus, the leverage is of the order of 350 to 1 for cumulative growth, and 50 to 1 for potential profit. This makes it clear that a very few, even one, really creative individual can exert a tremendous influence on the future of an enterprise.

The equations for these curves are:

Logistic curve:
$$y = \frac{K}{1 + be^{-at}}$$

$$y = \frac{K}{1 + e^{f-at}} \qquad \text{where } f = ln\ b$$

$$y = \frac{K}{1 + z} \qquad \text{where } z = e^{f-at}$$

$$\frac{dy}{dt} = \frac{Kaz}{(1 + z)^2} \qquad = y\,\frac{az}{1 + z} = y'$$

$$\frac{d^2y}{dt^2} = \frac{Ka^2z(z - 1)}{(1 + z)^3} \qquad = y'\,\frac{a(z - 1)}{(1 + z)} = y''$$

$$\frac{d^3t}{dt^3} = \frac{Ka^3z(1 - 4z + z^2)}{(1 + z)^4} \qquad = y''\,\frac{a(1 - 4z + z^2)}{(z - 1)(1 + z)}$$

External conditions never stay the same. The old competitive product may be improved, and fight back, and this reduces the original future potential. It does not, however, vitiate the principle; it merely reduces the initial advantage. In the course of time, either the market becomes saturated or new products or processes are developed which equal or surpass the currently ascendant one, and so its growth slows down, levels off, and ultimately declines in the face of the new, more efficient product or process.

In order to show the relationship involved, we started with the logistic curve and constructed successively its first, second, and third derivatives (Fig. 6:4). In so doing, we were actually working the problem backward. The sequence in real life is reversed. Human ingenuity is applied constructively to the solution of some socio-economic problem. The constructive effort used in seeking a solution, the conceiving of the idea that embodies an improved solution to the problem, and the continued effort to work out and apply the idea—all together constitute the first hump or positive lobe of the third derivative. The economic effectiveness of the idea is indicated by the positive value of the curve; the greater the inherent increase

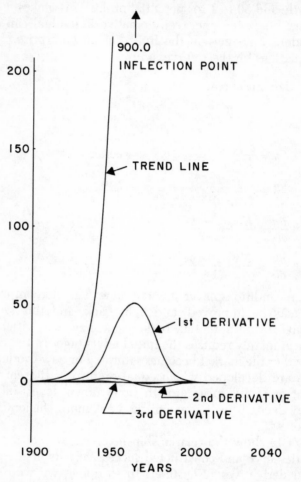

Fig. 6:5 LOGISTIC CURVE, SHOWING QUANTITATIVE RELATIONSHIP OF DERIVATIVES

in economic efficiency, the larger the positive value of the third derivative.

As progress is made in working out the details and applying

the new concept, the potential profit begins to rise above the average for the industry and this potential profit will exceed the average in proportion as the economic saving is large. Thus, the potential or driving force that resides in the idea as a result of its economic utility establishes the relative or differential profit position, and this is the second derivative.

What invites the expenditure of effort in research and development is the inherent value of the idea. This is not only the incentive that enlists the financial support of the organization that supports the research, but also is a key factor in the motivation of the researcher himself. He—and, in fact, we all—want to be engaged in constructive, important work. Moreover, the advantage in profits of the new idea over existing products or processes is what entices the risking of capital necessary to build and expand the plant, and other capital facilities required to commercialize the idea.

As the details and refinements of the idea are worked out, as the production problems are worked out, and distribution problems are solved, the potential profit expressed by the *first* derivative expands, and as a result, capacity and sales continually increase. The logistic or growth curve indicates the sum of the contribution of the application of the idea.

At some stage, most of the problems involved in commercializing the idea are solved. Creative effort directed toward the product or process diminishes, as indicated by the declining portion of the curve for the third differential. The fact that the ∂x^3 curve goes below zero does not mean that negative research is directed toward the project. The base line is not an absolute zero, but rather, it represents an average or norm with respect to creative attention in the field in general. Each idea is evaluated against alternatives, against a base that is constantly shifting upward with general progress, and the fighting-for-survival of alternate processes.

As creative effort for the given product or process decreases, it will finally fall below the average, as is indicated by the area in which the third derivative becomes negative. This is the stage during which the competition is consolidating for a major assault, but the danger is not yet evident to the complacent operator with his eye on a rewarding present. Finally, the gradual loss of relative advantage becomes evident to everyone and renewed creative attention is directed to the product to try to "save the day." This is the period of the second positive node on the third derivative curve. Of course, by this time it is very late, and usually the fighting back succeeds only in preventing a rout—in merely stabilizing the position for awhile. We see evidence of such a fight-back in the rayon industry in its competition with the newer synthetics; and in leather, as it attempts to fight off competition from plastics.

It is probable that in most cases it would be more profitable to abandon a product in the latter stages of its history, when its profit position is deteriorating. A better return would result from investing research and capital in newer projects with more potential, rather than in expending effort to fight back. This becomes a very difficult decision for management. As the sales volume of the product is already big, the initial stages of the fight-back may pay sizable dividends. Unfortunately, precisely because sizable investment is at stake and because of the very prevalent human resistance to change, altogether too much of money and effort is likely to be directed into trying to save a dying product. Consequently, enough effort is committed in trying to shore up the position so that the curve for logistic growth continues to its predicted asymptote.

The stages indicated by the different sections of the third derivative follow through in the life cycle of a product, a class of products, an industry, a company or other organization, or even a nation. There are cases where a rebirth has occurred to revitalize a maturing product or organization. For example, the growth in consumption of copper was lifted to a new and faster rate by the needs of the electric age. In similar manner, a mature lead industry was revitalized by the introduction of the lead storage battery.

In selecting projects, the research director will do well to avoid spending too big a portion of his budget on old products. Of course, he will have no choice if his research group does not come up with worthwhile new ideas. This will not be a problem if the researchers are informed about company objectives and understand the value of fundamental labor-saving ideas. In many cases, the director will have to do a constant selling job on top management to transfer enough of their attention from the short-range to the longer-range view. Most of all, he will need a few men in his group and in top management that are genuinely creative, that have vision, and think BIG. This is the essential catalyst needed to keep the organization active, to prevent early stagnation, and avoid becoming immersed and drowned in the everyday detail.

A study of profits at various stages in the life cycle of a product shows that, ideally, in order to maximize the return on investment, it would appear best to enter a field at a point about one-fifth of the way up the growth curve. At this point, commercial use is beginning to expand, sales will increase rapidly so that profits will quickly show a good return on the investment. Entering at this stage lets some pioneer suffer many of the headaches and the expense of the early stages of development and the long delay in the recovery of research dollars through profits. There is just one major difficulty with such a tactic: the position probably will be well hedged in by patents. If the would-be newcomer can license, the patent hurdle may be no serious handicap; but if not, he will be frozen out.

Management should always consider the alternative of buying research through the outright purchase of patents or by licensing. The royalties will usually be found to be in line with the costs of research when capitalized and calculated to the present value of future income.

Buy or License Patents

The whole question of patents and research is becoming a very complicated problem for research management. The company that does the original research presumably will attain a strong patent position and enjoy a period of monopoly as specified by patent law. It often happens, however, that by the time the development work has fully prepared the product or process and the market has expanded enough to become profitable, the patent period has expired. The more fundamental and basic the development, the more this is likely to be so. The first producer may still have an advantage for a few additional years through know-how that he has developed and through his position in the market.

There is yet another factor worthy of consideration. Particularly with a radically new product, it may be that two or more competitors will actually develop the market faster than would one. Any one company or development group may become overengrossed in one approach to the use-and-distribution phase of the problem and neglect other important uses. A second independent group is almost certain to have a somewhat different approach. This may result in a synergistic effect and give a faster growth than an equal effort at development by one producer. Management might conclude that, in some cases, early licensing would return better over-all profits than maintaining a monopolistic position.

Whereas one or more aggressive competitors may well improve the investor's return by expanding the market more quickly, excessive competition at early stages may eliminate worthwhile profit for all. Under such conditions, later growth will be stunted because capital will shy away from a low-profit project. Studies of the history and rewards from Nylon, polyvinyl chloride, polyethylene, magnesium, the different antibiotics, and other major modern developments can give some excellent indications of the results from different approaches to the market.

Government and Business

Perhaps we should call attention to one more aspect of the patent problem. It grows out of the increasing complexity of our technology and the changing attitude in this country toward the proper relation between government and business. Today we find that many projects are too large for a small, or even a medium-sized, company to undertake. If such a project is successfully completed by a large company, this very success makes the company subject to attack as a monopolist. The research director and corporate management should expect the growing antibusiness trend to continue. It may not be many years before the patentee will be faced with compulsory licensing. This definite possibility, coupled with the fact that the government is now doing more than half of the total research, suggests that research management needs to re-examine the probable trend of the whole business-government relationship.

TYPES OF PROJECTS

The foregoing gives some of the criteria for selecting good projects and some of the basis for judging the appropriate time for entering a given field. There are other factors, however, that also need to be considered in the selecting of a problem. These are factors that relate to the size and nature of the research organization. Attention must also be given to the question of long-range *versus* short-range projects, fundamental *versus* applied research, the economy of the company, and social and political trends.

The particular combination of company objectives constitute what is sometimes called the *personality* or *philosophy* of the organization. All this should be taken into account in selecting research projects. Equally important is consideration of the economics of the organization. This encompasses the whole field of raw materials and supplies, locations of plants, by-products, marketing know-how, and other factors. For example, an improvement in the processing of steel might well be of little interest to a drug company. This is, of course, a rather extreme example, but many a good project has been turned down by this type of fundamental—although more subtle—incompatibility.

The importance and variety of personalities in companies becomes evident if one contrasts the extremes. Compare, for example, a novelty merchandise company with a power utility. For the company with experience and success in merchandising to consumers, the research management will want to give special attention to products for consumers. If the company is quick-footed in the market, it can successfully exploit a new product and drop it a little later when public interest lags. Other companies have not proved successful in selling to the ultimate consumer. Possibly research should emphasize more of the basic products that are sold to other industry.

Match Problem and Objective

Companies that are vertically integrated present some special problems to research management. Such a company must, of necessity, keep costs low in basic processes. As the source of basic or raw material is captive, the position becomes a real handicap if the process does not remain competitive. The research department will want to examine and re-examine these basic processes to keep them competitive. The integrated company also has opportunities to profit from multiple use of subassemblies and parts. In the process industries like chemicals, byproducts offer a fruitful field to explore. Some coproducts that are being used may not be upgraded to their best advantage. Byproducts and coproducts can be of utmost importance. For example, a company that sets out to make synthetic ammonia and has to make hydrogen from natural gas for its process, will earn less profit than a competitor that has byproduct hydrogen available from another process.

The lone researcher must face the same basic problem of objective. In selecting problems, he too should know where he is headed. Is he interested most in gaining quick recognition from his colleagues? If so, he will want to focus on smaller projects in order to achieve numerous publications. Is he interested in more fundamental scientific advancement? Such a project might take years to complete, but it offers its own type of reward. Or perchance, is the young researcher anxious to build a consulting practice? If so, this will influence his choice of projects.

Another factor in the selection of a problem is the choice between long-range and short-range research, between fundamental research and refinement. Many factors are involved in this decision, and ideally, projects will be chosen with an eye to the best balance in all the factors.

The research staff will have an influence on this aspect of selecting a problem. Some researchers are best at solving more fundamental, basic problems; others are best at developmental work. The factor of morale also enters. An organization, as well as the individuals in the organization, needs occasional successes. Successfully completing a project gives the researcher a psychological lift. If the whole laboratory is involved only in long-range, fundamental research, there will be long periods when no tangible results are evident. This is apt to be somewhat discouraging and may dull the keenness of interest. Occasionally it will be better to have a short-range project where at least some of the individuals in the research laboratory are finding answers. If the laboratory or research group is a new one that has not proved itself, it will want to produce quick results to demonstrate to management the value of research. This would indicate that shorter-range problems should be attacked first so that results can show quickly. In any case, the research group will want to tackle the best ideas at hand. There may not be a really good long-range project in view at some particular moment.

Other factors involve being sure that enough projects are coming from the laboratory so that management can select the most desirable or profitable ones. A company management would not be making full use of research opportunities if its laboratory were offering so few projects that the company felt an urge to invest in all of them. Along this line, a research director should keep in mind the balance in short-term *versus* long-term requirements of capital to utilize the results of the research.

The question is often raised, "How much research?" What part of a company's income should be spent on research? These are very practical questions which have to be solved in the practical world of business management. Unfortunately, there is no known formula for arriving at the correct answer. It is generally assumed, more or less correctly, that plowing back more dollars into research now will lead to faster growth of sales and earnings in the future. It is immediately obvious that, even if the stockholders were willing to forego all current income, management must strike a balance between returns to stockholders from current earnings and investment in research for increased future earnings. The most important factor to keep in mind in this connection, however, is the fact that the number of dollars spent in research is not a true measure of results to be expected. Some individual researchers and some research organizations accomplish a great deal more than others with a given amount of expenditure. The record shows that selection of a good problem is actually more important than just how many dollars are spent for research.

MARKET RESEARCH

Many research managements do market research or turn to the Market Research Department of their organization to make studies for them. These studies are then used as a basis of selecting fields in which to do research.

Unmet Needs

If such studies are to be made, they should be very broad, and in stating the problem, use should be made of an over-all and an intermediate objective. Consideration should be given to the class of product involved, its competition, potential substitutes, and the economy and raw material of these competitive or substitute products. All the various factors should be considered. For example, in studies on man-made synthetic fibers, consideration should be given to the alternative use of land for food production. As population increases, arable land will become increasingly required for food. Its value for food production may then make its alternative use for production of natural fibers too costly.

If the research director does not himself have a flair for practical economics, he will perhaps want a man on his staff to help in selecting suitable fields for research. Such an individual ought to have technical competence in the field of science or engineering, depending on the field of research, and a flair for practical economics. In this we are not talking about the theory of economics, but rather, intuition about the "thermodynamics" inherent in economic alternatives. This is a skill that is rather uncommon, but it is of utmost utility in sizing up a project in respect to its social usefulness.

I am reminded of an occurrence at the beginning of World War II. The Press and the Congress of the United States debated for months about the advisability of alternative methods of producing butadiene for synthetic rubber. One method used petroleum as a raw material; the other, ethanol. Hundreds of thousands of words were spoken and written on the question without seeming to approach an answer. Then one day a scientist, with this flair for practical economics, pointed out that the cost of ethanol (then 80 to 90¢ per gallon) was the true measure of the human effort that went into producing the alcohol. We were exceedingly short of manpower for the war effort, so obviously we needed processes that required the minimum of manpower. As butadiene from petroleum was much cheaper, this meant less manpower per pound of rubber.

Also involved in the selection of a problem is the question of sources of ideas. Should the research organization work mostly on ideas suggested by the individual researchers themselves? Or should many of the ideas come from outside the laboratory? The source of an idea is unimportant if it is a good one. One important source of ideas which should not be overlooked is the salesman. He is constantly hearing from his customers about the problems which they have, or the difficulties and short-comings of the product. Feeding this information back to the laboratory may result in worthwhile ideas for improvement. The best source of ideas is probably the researchers themselves. If for no other reason than the simple question of motivation, the idea is a better one to work on if the researcher thought of it himself—if it is his idea.

Research management can do much to assist researchers to come up with the right kind of problems on which to work. Research management can "sell" the researcher on the objectives and philosophy of the company and can keep the laboratory worker informed on the company's basic economics. In these circumstances the researchers will be in tune with the company's objectives and in touch with its problems. They are quite apt to propose and to wish to work on problems of real interest to the organization. The research director should take the trouble to give his workers a view of the larger picture. The broader the researcher's knowledge of the general objectives, the more constructive he can be. In such an environment there are bound to be good ideas from the bottom and the best possible atmosphere for acceptance of suggestions at the top.

chapter 7

SELECTING
THE RESEARCHER

The two essential factors in research are problems and people. It is customary to associate research with laboratories, but when we look at it fundamentally, we find the following sequence. First, there must be a problem; secondly, there must be an individual who will try to solve the problem. Only then do we become concerned with the tools that the researcher may use.

To place the problem first and the researcher second may seem a little surprising. Is it not common for a research director to say that a good man will find his own problem? True enough, but the problem had to be there before he could find it.

In research management, the selection of personnel is without doubt second only in importance to selecting a problem. The selection of personnel has two phases: one has to do with hiring; and the other with placement, i.e., with matching the individual to the job in the research organization.

Selecting the individual at the hiring stage is an important task facing research management, and it is not a simple one. In building a research organization, the manager must concern himself with varying combinations of intelligence, interest, aptitude, and training. He needs to relate these various factors in a way that will balance the research group so they do a superior job of problem-solving and inventing. So important is this job of initial selection that some research managers believe that the die is cast once the selection is made. These managers believe that there is little that can be done to improve efficiency in research beyond hiring good men and giving them lots of freedom. Whether or not one accepts this attitude, there is no doubt about the importance of selection.

In approaching the problem of selecting personnel, research management must first establish for itself reasonably clear-cut objectives. The manager will have decided in what general field of science and engineering the efforts are to be centered. The work force will be different, depending on whether the organization is interested in aircraft, electronics, chemicals, or horticulture. Chemists, physicists, and engineers might be useful in all of these fields, but most certainly in different ratios. Modern concepts of the team approach suggest that any sizable research group would have personnel with training in a great variety of scientific and engineering fields. Having determined the general field and the broad objectives of the research organization, management will be in a position to build a staff that collectively represents a rounded and balanced training suitable for dealing with anticipated problems.

College Grades

It has long been characteristic for employment managers to place great emphasis on high grades, usually preferring personnel in the top 10% of college classes. There is something to be said for this practice because the same aptitude, capacity, interest, and hard work that results in high grades in college classes will probably be an asset in later years. There have, in fact, been a number of studies that show substantial correlation between college grades and later success.

Success in the workaday world is usually measured in terms of dollar income. Correlation between grades and income may mean merely that there is a correlation between good grades and a tendency to enter management careers, and hence, in later years, to draw higher salaries. One of the factors that lead to high grades is a high capacity for conformity and for following the wishes of the professor. This type of behavior pattern is a bar to creativity. A number of our most creative people—men like Thomas A. Edison, the Mayo brothers, Buckminster Fuller, to mention a few—could not adjust themselves to the slow pace of our school curriculum. These and other facts indicate that grades alone are an inadequate basis for selecting research personnel.

I.Q. Scores

If grades are a poor criterion of creativity, I.Q. rating is even less indicative. As work by J. P. Guilford and others has shown (Chapter 3), the type of intellectual response measured by I.Q. tests is only one of many, and is not closely correlated with creativity. Researchers Getzel and Jackson, of the University of Chicago, and Torrance at Minnesota, report that in their tests the selecting of top-level individuals on the basis of I.Q. missed 70% of the individuals that were in the top 20% in creativity. Clearly, I.Q. rating should not be of first concern for the research recruiter.

In our highly developed modern technology and the group approach to research, it also appears that many jobs in a research organization do not call for high creativity, but do require a scientific training and a degree of competence. A well-organized research group will need members that are staunch, steady workers to supplement the more brilliant, creative but sometimes flighty, members. This is the old question of Indians and chiefs. An organization that is all chiefs will suffer from lack of Indians to do the more routine work.

The more clearly management can establish its objective in research and the intended assignment to a prospective researcher, the better it is prepared to tackle the problem of selection. In addition to examining the excellence of formal training, management will want to know as much as possible about the aptitudes, temperament, and interests of the applicant. A behavior pattern that is ideal for a development engineer will be far from ideal for a fundamental researcher; or, by contrast, for a technical salesman. The interest profile and behavior pattern of the individual are perhaps more important than the formal training. The lack of certain desirable courses can be remedied by extra study; but work habits, interests, temperament, and behavior change only slowly. Selection, not reform, is the proper function in staffing a research department.

Various tests and techniques have been devised which can be used to improve our understanding of individual preferences and their significance. We are not concerned here with trivial differences, as for example, "Does a man prefer bridge to poker?" What is important are the underlying habits and reaction patterns that are an essential part of the individual's way of life. If the work situation does not match these, the individual will be unhappy even though he may be reasonably competent at performing the work. If he is not comfortable and happy in his work, the motivation—that all-essential ingredient of creativity—will be reduced.

Attention can now be directed to some of the techniques for improving the selection and for the matching of the prospective researcher to the job. John Mills, in Chapters 2, 3, and 4 of his excellent book, *The Engineer in Society*,[1] has emphasized the importance of interests and has reported some of the procedures that he used successfully for years at the Bell Telephone Laboratories to select the "natural" researchers.

S-D Types

One of his techniques involved discovering the natural approach of the prospective employee when confronted with a problem. He noticed a reaction pattern which characteristically differentiated individuals that had an aptitude for research. He found that most individuals could be classified as either an S-type or D-type. The S-type is usually good at research. The D-type seldom is; his characteristic approach is more like that of a businessman, an entertainer, or a politician.

Mills used the term "S-type" to indicate an individual who, in sizing up a situation and making comparisons, habitually and characteristically thinks of the similarities first. The "D-type" referred to an individual who thinks of the differences first.

Psychological association tests have confirmed his notion that this characteristic of human reaction has a bimodal rather than a normal distribution. There are a few individuals that are somewhere between the S and D types, and that think of similarities and differences more or less alternately. This important reaction pattern on the part of individuals may change somewhat with time, particularly with changed environment and experiences, but for the most part it appears to be so fundamental

---

[1] D. Van Nostrand Co. Inc., New York, 1946.

that it is important to give it consideration in selecting individuals for research.

Psychological tests have been prepared which can be used to evaluate the individual with respect to this important characteristic. For all practical purposes, however, comparatively simple on-the-spot tests appear to be reasonably adequate. For example, the prospective employee may be asked to compare the pen and pencil in a companion set. Confronted with this problem, the S-type individual will characteristically say something like this: "They are both writing instruments; they are both long, cylindrical objects; they are both made of plastic and metal; they are made by the same company." And then he will turn his attention to the differences, pointing out that one is a pen and the other a pencil, that perhaps one is a little larger in diameter, and one is a little longer, etc. The D-type individual, by contrast, will first note the differences and later turn his attention to the similarities.

A second "reading" might be obtained by asking for a comparison of two similar magazines. Let us say, for example, *Business Week* and *Chemical Week*, or *Newsweek* and *Time* magazines. With a little ingenuity it is easy to find a variety of objects at hand that have the appropriate degree of similarity, and that can be used to discover the individual's characteristic reaction to the problem of comparisons.

The characterization of S-type and D-type essentially differentiates between individuals that are inductive thinkers and those that are deductive. The S-type, or inductive thinker, is the logician. He sees the common thread in apparently unrelated happenings. From his observations and experiences he synthesizes and develops generalizations and laws. He has an inner urge to develop order out of chaos. Philosophers, logicians, scientists, and mathematicians are characteristically S-type individuals.

The D-type is by nature a deductive thinker. He goes from the general to the specific. His tendency to focus on differences gives him a basis for choosing between alternate courses of action. Whereas the S-type is hindered, in a sense immobilized, by his attention to similarities, the D-type makes decisions easily. Men of action, such as businessmen, lawyers,

politicians, entertainers, and salesmen, are characteristically
D-type individuals.

Interest and the Job

Of importance also is the individual's interests in life. Interests may be indicated in a variety of ways, and the value of
each will depend on the purpose of the rating. For purposes of
hiring, there is no need to use the elaborate preference ratings
used in vocational guidance. The need, rather, is for the broader
classification that will indicate basic response patterns which
can then be related to the job situation. One simple scale would
rate an individual's interests with respect to whether they were
primarily in ideas, things, or people. Some individuals are most
competent and best satisfied when dealing with human and
emotional relationships. Other individuals are most apt and
content when dealing with material things and concrete situations. A much smaller portion of our society are competent
and satisfied when dealing with ideas and with abstractions,
whether these be words or symbols. They like to generalize with
theory about either our animate or our inanimate universe.

Mills found these tendencies important and for his own use
further elaborated abstractions by indicating two types: ideas,
and dollar symbols. He pictured an individual as an artist paint-
ing on the canvas of life. And he pictured the practitioner of
any career—whether that of an artist, an engineer, or a scientist—as expressing his personality through working on some
medium. For a singer the medium would be his voice; for another musician it would be his instrument; for the painter it
would be oil or water colors on canvas; for the sculptor it would
be clay, marble, or bronze.

Mills then states: "For the nonartistic professions there may
be distinguished four media, namely, 1) ideas, 2) men, 3)
things, 4) $ symbols." Of these, men and things are concrete;
ideas and symbols are abstract. The philosopher and pure mathematician are examples of those whose medium is ideas. Politicians, missionaries, writers, and advertisers are concerned
with expressing themselves through their influence on men.
Statistical economists, bankers, and treasurers express themselves characteristically through dollar symbols.

Some of these examples illustrate reasonably clear-cut, uncomplicated media interests. These are extreme and limiting cases, however. Most men have overlapping interests. By listing the individual's interest in these four types of media in descending order of preference, Mills arrived at seven interest types for nonartistic professions. The following table shows his seven types and their characteristics:

Table 7:1

TYPES OF CAREERS IN NONARTISTIC PROFESSIONS

	Order of Interest			
	1st	2nd	3rd	Last
1. Physical-research	ideas	things	men	$ symbols
2. Physical-development	things	ideas	men	$ symbols
3. Technical-management	things	men	ideas	$ symbols
4. Management-technical	men	things	ideas	$ symbols
5. Economic-research	ideas	$ symbols	men	things
6. Human-relations	men	ideas	things	$ symbols
7. Business management	men	$ symbols	things	ideas

Mills then characterizes each of the seven types in the following manner:

1. The *Physical-Research Type* would have as a prime objective the extension of physical principles. Such an individual prefers technical responsibilities rather than supervisory responsibilities; he would, in fact, generally make a poor supervisor.
2. The *Physical-Development Type* would have primary concern with the development of equipment and processes. Such individuals would also prefer technical responsibilities.
3. The *Technical-Management Type* indicates a primary interest in technical processes and a secondary interest in management. Such an individual will be best suited for supervisory responsibilities in a plant requiring technical understanding and judgments. These individuals will ordinarily advance in an organization based primarily on technical interests and competence, but supplemented by interest in human relations.
4. The *Management-Technical Type* is primarily interested in management and secondarily only in processes and technical things. Such individuals prefer supervisory responsibilities; and are well fitted to manage in organizations

where relatively large numbers of workers make the human relations problem more important than technical problems.

5. The *Economic-Research Type* prefers technical responsibilities involving, however, dollar symbols rather than mechanical equipment. These individuals make good industrial economists, consultants on financial problems, and controllers.

6. The *Human-Relations Type* indicates individuals whose interests fit them especially for research in human relations, problems of management, or frequently, religious or social work.

7. The *Business-Management Type* is concerned primarily with commercial relations. These individuals make good salesmen and business managers. They prefer a supervisory responsibility; they have high economic motivation, and in general, a low interest in mechanical things and craftsmanship.

This approach and the previous one are suggested as helpful ways of examining a prospective researcher to see whether his interests and characteristic reaction pattern really suit him for the proposed research job. These are not tests that can be administered by the inexperienced and machine-scored, but they can be helpful to the experienced interviewer in improving his selection. Two techniques may be useful: carefully designed probing questions; and asking the applicant to rate his relative interests.

There are many other means for gaining insight into the individual's preferences. There are, for example, interest appraisals such as the *Kruder Preference Test*, the *Strong Vocational Interest Record*, and the *Allport-Vernon Study of Values*. These, however, do not seem to lend themselves very readily to the environment of an actual interview and the selecting of an employee for research work; their utility lies more in the area of vocational guidance.

CREATIVITY

The really key question concerning a prospective researcher is, "How creative will he be?" It is easy enough to look about and pick out individuals that have been creative in their various fields. It is much more difficult, however, to discover why they are creative, and how they differ from noncreative people, many of whom are highly educated. Fortunately, however, in recent years some progress has been made in discovering some of the meaningful, differentiating characteristics of creative individuals, and in tests for rating individuals in these characteristics.

Professor Viktor Lowenfeld, who heads the Department of Art Education at Pennsylvania State University, has been working for some years to solve the riddle of creativity. He appears to have made significant progress. One of his former students, Dr. W. Lambert Brittain at Cornell University, has also contributed to our understanding of this important problem. Whereas these two men center their attention more specifically on the arts, Professor J. P. Guilford at the University of Southern California, has been conducting similar studies on creativity in science. His work led him to identify eight differentiating attributes of creative persons. His list proved to be almost identical with the findings at Penn State. The striking similarity between the findings of these two independent studies suggests that creative individuals do, in fact, have some common attributes. Eight attributes that seem to be important are:

1. Sensitivity
2. Fluency
3. Flexibility
4. Originality
5. Skill at redefinition
6. Ability to abstract
7. Ability to synthesize
8. Coherence of organization

Subsequent research may show that these are not the only important ones, or in fact that some other combination of attributes will give a better indication. From the practical point of view, however, the important thing is that tests have been developed by which individuals can be ranked in these eight attributes. Accordingly, a start has been made in being able to identify the creative individual by testing procedures.

Sensitivity

According to Dr. Lowenfeld, the creative person exhibits an unusual degree of sensitivity to problems, to needs, to attitudes, and feelings of other persons, and to the experiences of life. Such an individual has trained himself, in the words of Dr. Lowenfeld, "to use his eyes not only for seeing but for observing, his ears not only for hearing but for listening, and his hands not only for touching but for feeling." The creative individual has a keen awareness of anything odd or promising in the situation, the material, or the person with whom he is dealing.

Repeated studies have indicated that there is little, if any, difference between perceptual and social sensitivity. Both of these types of sensitivity can be tested. One of the tests for perceptual sensitivity was developed by the late Professor L. L. Thurstone of the University of Chicago. He tests the ability to recognize a word in which part of each letter has been erased.

Social sensitivity—that is, the ability to identify problems in human relations—is often tested by giving the subject a statement of a present-day trend and asking him to list possible effects of this trend at some future time. For example, one might use a statement like this: "More girls have been born in the past five years than boys. What effect will this have twenty years from now (in addition to the obvious effect that there will be more women than men)?" Obviously, the type of answers given will indicate social sensitivity.

Fluency

Fluency is defined by Dr. Lowenfeld as "the ability to take continuous advantage of a developing situation . . ." Studies on a large number of distinguished writers, painters, sculptors, and composers indicate that they do not begin with an elaborately preconceived plan. They start with an idea and develop it step by step. Frequently, the masterpiece is not the result of one masterful creation but the summation of progressive creations as each new problem is met.

Flexibility

Flexibility indicates the ability to adjust quickly and easily to new situations and unforeseen developments. If a truly creative sculptor's chisel slips, he will frequently turn the error into an asset instead of accepting defeat. In meeting unforeseen obstacles, the creative person displays flexibility much greater than the noncreative individual. Dr. Lowenfeld sometimes has his art students sketch murals. After their rough draft is completed, they are likely to find that they have been assigned a wall space that is in the corner or is broken by some ugly object such as a radiator or pipe. The creative student shows flexibility by modifying his plans to turn the obstacle into some striking feature in the composition. This is the characteristic that makes a good researcher sensitive to side- or unexpected discoveries, sometimes called *serendipity* (see Chapter 2).

Originality

Originality would always be one of the characteristic attributes of a creative person. It is not so easy to see how one will determine the degree of an individual's native originality. One test that is gaining acceptance is to require the subject to list six unusual uses for some common object—as, for example, a newspaper. Ordinary uses such as "to start a fire" or "to wrap garbage" would get a low rating; more imaginative uses such as "to make up kidnap notes" would score high. Such tests must always be scored by a trained individual.

Skill at Redefinition

Redefinition refers to the skill of being able to rearrange ideas, concepts, people, and things. Professor Guilford would say, "to shift the function of objects and use them in new ways." It is generally believed that invention and new ideas are not, strictly speaking, wholly new, but are only rearrangements and new combinations of old information already in the individual's memory. It is obvious, therefore, that if one can gain insight into the individual's aptitude for redefinition, it would be of importance with respect to his creativity.

Penn State has developed a test to measure skill at redefinition. In this test the individual is given a problem and a list of five objects. He is told that one of the objects can be used to solve the problem and is warned that the solution may require ingenuity. The problem might be, for example, "to start a fire." The objects made available could be a fountain pen, an onion, a pocket watch, a light bulb, and a golf club. An individual with an aptitude for redefinition would note that the crystal of the pocket watch could be used as a burning glass. A series of questions for problems of this type have been devised at Penn State and are used to test this attribute.

Ability to Abstract

The ability to abstract really is the ability to analyze. It refers to proficiency in breaking down a problem or project and in seeing their relationships. It is by means of analysis that one can penetrate through to the core of a problem. Dr. Lowenfeld goes so far as to say that, "Without analysis, no truly creative work is possible . . . The noncreative person keeps looking at the old problem as one stubborn mass. The creative person starts breaking it down into bite-sized chunks the moment he sees it."

Several rather complicated tests are used at Penn State to measure this attribute. Simpler ones can be devised, however, based on the fact, verified by studies, that there is a close correlation between the ability to abstract and the observance of details of everyday environment. For example, "Where is the green signal on a vertical stop light?" The observant individual will be apt to have the correct answer for this question and others like it.

Ability to Synthesize

It is no surprise to find that aptitude for synthesis is related to creativity. Tests have been devised, based on such experiments as these: Present the subject with words in a scrambled order and ask him to combine them into a meaningful sentence; or give the subject a number of unrelated objects—for example, steel wool, strips of cardboard, pipe cleaners, tongue depressors, screen wire, and scraps of yarn—and ask him to combine them into an aesthetic three-dimensional composition. Obviously, these tests require an expert judge to administer them and to interpret the results.

Coherence of Organization

This attribute is the ability to organize a project or express an idea in such a way that nothing is superfluous. In a sense, we could say that it is the ability to apply the *Law of Parsimony*. In a test, designed by Dr. Alfred Kiesselbach at Penn State University, the subject is confronted with a series of designs arranged in pairs. In each pair both designs are abstract, but one combines the symbols in a more imaginative way, and it is the latter that the more creative individual will select.

By giving consideration to personality characteristics and by employing questions and simple tests to evaluate the applicant's interests and characteristic behavior patterns, the interviewer can improve techniques of selection in the hiring of prospective research workers. Each interviewer can develop a number of problem-type questions which will reveal something of the applicant's reactions to problem situations. One such question which has been used for prospective laboratory workers is: "How would you wire a double-pole, double-throw switch for reversing current flow?"

If the question is well designed, it can reveal more than the technical competence of the applicant. For example, an economist might be asked about foreign trade in this manner: "On a long-term basis, should our exports exceed our imports or should the imports exceed exports?" If the applicant is competent in economics, he will reply that the important thing is that the international account or payments must balance; and that hence, exports and imports must balance unless offset by services or movements of capital. Here the question is phrased so as to suggest a simple answer. If the applicant has knowledge in the field, self-reliance, and confidence, he will go beyond the barrier suggested by the statement of the question.

An important question, especially in the social sciences, is: "What books have you read recently? What current literature do you read?" The answer to these and questions about hobbies and leisure time can indicate a good deal about the likes and characteristics of the applicant.

The application of more extensive examination by interviewers trained in psychology and the application of more extensive psychological tests, such as the *Humm-Wadsworth Temperament Test,* will give a more complete picture of the behavior pattern of the prospective employee. These more extensive tests find their greatest usefulness, however, as an aid to better placement of the employee than as a means of selection. There is a tendency for psychological tests to emphasize the normal or more frequent type of behavior as desirable. Sometimes—

maybe most of the time—the truly creative individual will in some respects be an "oddball." If too much emphasis is placed on hiring "good guys," the most effective researchers may be rejected.

PLACEMENT

As has been indicated, the problem of selecting a researcher should not be isolated too much from the type of work to be assigned. Both tests and experience teach that some individuals are by nature "lone wolves." Others, on the other hand, are at their best when working with a team and when in close association with coworkers. These and other characteristics of researchers as individuals should be taken into account in assigning problems and in placing the individual in the research organization. Management should plan to bend the organization to fit the individual's needs and not try to warp the individual to a preconceived organizational scheme.

To get a reading on the individual's natural level of gregarious needs, Mills, when he set out to hire researchers, asked some simple questions. He found that he could determine the important differences by merely asking questions about the individual's natural inclinations. The type of question is illustrated by one that Alfred Harcourt used in attempting to select salesmen for his publishing company. "What would you do when you found yourself walking toward a college hall and straight ahead of you was a man you knew but not a close friend or a member of your class? Would you whistle and hurry to walk with him, or keep about the same distance behind?" [2] The extrovert, the salesman, would hurry to catch up.

Mills thought of work naturally dividing itself into two types: One in which the individual studies, creates, and carries on mental and physical routines; the other as collective work which involves contact with people—peers, superiors, or inferiors. He would first question the individual to see what fraction of his work period he would prefer to spend in collective activity and what part in individual effort. Then he would seek to subdivide the two.

---

[2] In Mills, *op. cit.*, p. 26.

Under individual activity he used the subheadings:

> *Study Creativity*
> *Mental Routines*
> *Physical routines.*

Under the collective activities he used the headings:

> *Work with superiors*
> *Work with equals*
> *Work with inferiors.*

By "superior" and "inferior" he is here referring to controlled relationships; the superior being the one having control, the inferior being the one controlled.

This is used in a broader sense and control here has broader implications than merely the intraorganizational relationships. For example, when a salesman is seeking an order from a customer, it is the customer that exercises the control; and therefore, in this relationship, he would be thought of as a superior, no matter what the status of the two might be on any other basis. Research by its very nature requires considerable individual work. By paying attention to this aspect of the individual's behavior pattern, work can be assigned more effectively.

In the assignment of individuals within the research organization, management should seek maximum attainment of two different objectives. One is placement that satisfies the researcher; and the other is the building of effective, creative subunits within the organization. As will be discussed in more detail in subsequent chapters, this will involve combinations of individuals with different basic training, as well as with characteristically different approaches to problems. Every research organization needs idea men to dream up enough projects so that management may select the most promising ones for more intensive study. At least some of the idea men should have enough drive to stir up the organization. They will be most effective if their ideas—and maybe even their tactics—annoy others in the laboratory. The more complacent researchers will then work harder and come through with better ideas in self-defense. If the research management wants a really effective group, it may be desirable to plan to have at least one individual around who is a kind of "thorn in the side" and who is always "rocking the boat."

Another aspect of assigning jobs to employees is worth mentioning. An individual, who after a few years changes to a new field of research, or at least to a new corner in his chosen field, often has his creativity regenerated. Moving individuals at reasonable intervals from one type of research to problems in related fields has merit but will take careful planning. Researches on creativity and practical experience indicate that planned changes in job assignments will improve ideas and performance. In planning these changes, it will probably develop that some individual should be shifted out of the research laboratory into production, or product development, or some other type of activity for which a technical background is helpful but for which creativity in the inventive sense is not of predominant importance. This is one of the ways in which research management has through the years kept the average age in research laboratories from becoming progressively higher and higher.

A Creative Environment

We should perhaps remind ourselves at this point concerning one other problem associated with creativity and native ability. Not much is known as yet about how the young child develops into a creative adult. It seems highly probable, however, that along with native intelligence and aptitudes which fit the individual for a creative role in society, environmental factors may also have an important influence. It is fine for a research management to use the very latest and most effective tools in trying to select creative young researchers. If, however, such researchers after being hired find themselves in an organization that does not reward nor respect creativity—in an environment that is not conducive to creativity—it is highly probable that the creative individual either will leave the organization or his creativity will atrophy through disuse. If research management is interested in having highly creative researchers, it will need to give attention to creating the right organization and morale to reinforce the creative tendencies of the researcher himself.

chapter 8

THE RESEARCH
ORGANIZATION

Organization has to do with the WHO question: *Who* does
what, and *when?* Wherever two or more persons wish to combine their efforts on a given project, organization is involved.
It may be formal or informal, highly structured or loosely knit.
Experience indicates that the nature of the organization, the
way it operates, and the type and quality of its leadership,
will have considerable influence on the effectiveness of the
group.

In the most fundamental sense, the objective of organization
is to maximize the synergistic effect of cooperative effort in a
group. Properly organized, a group will produce more than the
sum of an equal number of individual efforts. The extent of this
synergism may be very large. K. K. Paluev[1] equates the rise of
the modern technical age with the group approach to research
and development. He indicates that production of a machine,
a book, or a mathematical formula involves three elements of
human nature: ideas, emotions, and actions. The progress that
results depends on success in correlating and organizing these
elements.

He further points out that progress—i.e., new inventions,
new products, new processes—requires changes in these three
factors; it requires new ideas, new emotional responses or at-
tachments, and some new action. He then postulates that a
number of independent faculties must be simultaneously

---

[1] K. K. Paluev, How collective genius contributes to industrial progress; reprinted with revisions from *General Electric Review*, May 1941.

brought to bear to effect the required changes in ideas, emotions, and actions. He mentions fifteen such faculties, among which are the following:

Creative discontent
Originality
Courage
Specific knowledge
Analytical ability
Ability to synthesis
Enthusiasm
Energy
Initiative

If these faculties or traits are independent, and if, as seems probable, they are distributed among us at random, a very interesting conclusion follows. The chance that any on individual would have outstanding aptitude in all the faculties required to conceive, develop, and "put across" important new ideas is rather small. According to Paluev's calculations, about ONE individual in 50,000,000 would have excellence in ten of the fifteen faculties, if by "excellence" we mean that he would be the best in a group of six. Thus, the over-all genius is indeed a very rare individual. If several individuals, however, each with excellence in one or a few of the desired faculties, can pool their efforts, they may be able to accomplish much the same results as a genius might. This, then, is the nature of the synergism that can be obtained by good organization. Plainly, what is needed is a research organization so managed that it will give maximum synergy.

Objectives

In considering the organization, it is important to take account of: 1) division of labor; 2) use of experimental equipment—some of which is expensive; 3) psychological factors in interpersonal and group relations. Also, there is need to consider the different types of individuals and the proper proportion of each in a well-balanced organization.

Another factor which should be given prime consideration by management in setting up a research organization is the built-in timing. Does the organization as such diminish or increase the length of time between idea and commercialization? If the results of research can be put to work quickly, it will start to make profits which will thus compound more rapidly. Because of the compound interest effect, management should organize the research so as to telescope the research and development time to the minimum commensurate with adequate testing. Dr. Turner Alfrey, Jr.,[2] in an unpublished paper, has made calculations which show that, under certain conditions, halving the time to commercialization may be twice as profitable to a company as would be the doubling of expenditures for research. Thus, if management wishes to realize its maximum returns from research, it will have to give attention to organizational relationships all the way from the researcher at the bench through pilot plant and market-testing activities, and finally, plant design and construction itself.

Authoritarian Type

On the basis of the power relations exhibited, it is easy to recognize three basic types of organization. One is the "dictator" or "authoritarian" type. In this type, communications are from the top down; the workers have mostly duties, and few privileges or rights.

It appears that the Germans, at least before World War II, were inclined to favor the authoritarian type of organization. The laboratory director assigned the projects and kept contact between the individual researchers to the minimum. Under such a system, the German chemical industry between World Wars I and II pushed to the forefront. By 1938, the I. G. Farben dominated many important fields. With this type of organization the industrial laboratories in Germany methodically covered every facet of any problem or product that concerned them. It proved successful for them.

In recent years the Russians seem to be doing very well in research, especially in certain fields where they are concentrating their interest. In all probability, theirs is also a highly structured, authoritarian type of organization.

For many years this type of organization was the accepted standard in business theory. In fact, this type of organization

---

[2] Dr. Turner Alfrey, Jr., *A Mathematical Model for Research-Induced Organizational Growth,* 1952; unpublished paper.

has been effectively used by many successful businesses, both past and present. Some believe that where a specific, definite goal is established, the military type of organization will always be most efficient. The findings of modern social psychologists throw considerable doubt on this, however. There appear to be two ways in which this type of organization falls short of maximum results. It limits important applications of creativity very largely to the director. If the director happens to be an "idea dynamo," the results may be very good; if he is not, the whole effort is apt to be merely routine. In any case, in the military-type organization little use would be made of the creativity of the individual researchers. They are limited to using their ingenuity in solving the fractions of the problems which are assigned to them.

The other weakness of the authoritarian approach is that it creates group conformities which tend to work counter to the objectives of management. As a result, the group effort will be something less than the best. What is clearly needed is an organization that takes full account of human nature and, at the same time, causes the efforts to be directed so completely toward the management's objectives that the desired result is achieved to maximum advantage.

At the opposite end of the scale is another type which might be thought of as "anarchy." Here there are only privileges but no duties. Somewhere in the middle we will find what we might choose to call "democracy." In this type of organization the duties will equal or balance the privileges.

We might picture the organization problem in this way. In anarchy everyone might well be pulling very hard but in all different directions, so that the resultant force equals zero. In an authoritarian organization all would pull in one direction but nobody would be pulling quite so hard as he could. The organizational objective is to get a high degree of ordering of effort toward management's objective without appreciably reducing the efforts of each individual.

R&D Must Be Directed

In recognition of the foregoing, many modern writers have said that "research cannot be directed." They have pictured the research director as a sort of counselor or father confessor. They picture him as unlike a supervisor in any other division of an organization. This sort of attitude goes too far in the direction of anarchy. This thinking confuses tactics and strategy. A *research director's job is to direct.* He has the primary responsibility of seeing that the right problems are being worked on. He must allocate the effort among problems. In the interest of over-all objectives, he must sometimes terminate work on a problem before it is solved. In performing these functions and in handling matters of budget and personnel, he does indeed direct the research.

Nor is this type of direction resented by researchers. For example, few research men resent being told what problem to work on; what they do resent and resist is being told how to do it. In fact, if the supervisor does a good job in giving the reason why when he presents a problem to one of his men, he will usually find the researcher eager to work on any problem that management considers important. The researcher is well aware that much of the recognition he attains, particularly in tangible form, comes from management. Hence, management's wish is a strong motivational factor for him; and for all practical purposes, the laboratory director is management. The problem is not whether the research director shall direct; the problem is *HOW?*

Occasionally, a research director may ask a researcher to work on a problem that it is plain to the latter is doomed to failure. He will certainly not work very hard on such a problem. He will, in all probability, mark time until some more promising project makes it convenient to lay aside the dud. Consider the researcher that worked for a laboratory director that was a real idea-man. He had more ideas in a week than most persons will have in a lifetime, but many were not good ones. One of his research men developed a technique. If asked to tackle some weird problem, he would postpone starting on it for a week. If during the week the director asked about the project, George would say that he was just getting started on it. If the director did not inquire about it within a week, George knew that the director had forgotten about it and so he did likewise.

This is related merely to elaborate the thought that most researchers quickly adjust to the "boss" and are not nearly so sensitive as is sometimes supposed. The key point is that the research director has the responsibility of seeing that the research advances the interests of the organization. He is the one individual in the whole research setup that has the broadest knowledge of the problems to be solved and of the aspirations of the organization. Ideally, he should communicate all this to each researcher, but to do this fully would leave little time for actual research. A workable compromise is required. Essentially, this consists in the director's doing a good job of selling the importance of the job when he assigns it; (see *Objective*, Chapter 2).

In selling the job, any good supervisor will give the reason why. This will generally be adequate to rouse the active interest of most researchers. There are, however, many refinements in the technique of "selling" a project. The laboratory head who knows his scientists well will readily vary the approach to suit the individual. Sometimes the director will need to spend time, perhaps hours, in a discussion in which he gets the researcher to think of the problem himself. The researcher is immediately motivated because, not realizing that the idea has been subtly suggested to him, thinks of it as his own idea.

There is yet another side to the problem of directing research. Any good research man will think of problems on his own. He would like to work on these problems. The pride of authorship makes them important to him. Some of these problems will not be worth the effort; others will not fit into the organization's economics or goals. Nevertheless, research management will need to give each idea a hearing. Discussion of the relation of the proposed project to over-all objectives and resources available will usually satisfy the researcher. If management shows a genuine interest in such ideas, it will encourage other ideas and suggestions, some of which will be good. In any case, whether the project was the researcher's own idea, whether he was led to think of it, or whether it was assigned to him, his supervisor should thereafter label it as the given research man's project and so report it to management.

STATUS OF RESEARCH IN ORGANIZATION

How should the research organization be arranged to ensure that it is more an aid than a handicap to efficiency in research? Where in the organization should research report? Many have wrestled with this problem and have finally begged the question by saying that the research director should report to that officer in top management who is most interested in research. This is certainly sound from the standpoint of the personalities involved, and it is certainly true that organization should adjust to, and be built around, the key men. Nevertheless, other things being equal, there is a natural place to attach research.

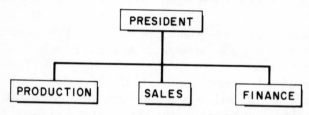

Fig. 8:1 CONVENTIONAL ORGANIZATIONAL CHART

Historically, theory on organization of the firm has focused attention on the three functions: PRODUCTION, SALES, and FINANCE. The basic structure of the organization chart has usually taken the form shown in Figure 8:1.

If RESEARCH is added, it is usually shown as a fourth independent unit, at the same organizational level as the three other functions.

This is not an adequate picture of the structure of an organization. For one thing, it shows no interrelation among the three functions. This could be remedied by placing these functions at the corners of a triangle.

If the president is thought of as the nucleus of the organization, the arrangement in Figure 8:2 places him at the center of gravity and with equal contact with the three functions. Moreover, this diagram shows contact and relationships among the three functions.

R&D—A Basic Function

There is a further difficulty which even this scheme does not avoid. This picture or chart is two-dimensional and as such has no depth. As any real organization has body it can be adequately pictured only in three dimensions. It is easy to see that any commercial organization must have production (of goods or services), must have sales (distribution), and must have finance. Is there anything else that is required for any real organization? Yes, there must be an *idea*. There must be the concept of the goods to be produced or the service to be performed—the idea toward which the other three factors are organized. The function of this idea is what the economists call the "entrepreneurial function." A new idea must satisfy a human need better than alternates or it will not be used. This integrating, salable idea is of fundamental importance to an organization. If we now add this to the basic organizational chart, we have a three-dimensional figure.[3]

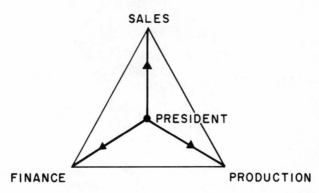

Fig. 8:2 Two-dimensional Chart of Intra-organizational Relationships

As research primarily performs the idea-generating function of an industrial organization, we can substitute the word *research* for *idea*. We now have the four primary and essential functions for a vital organization, each shown as related to and reacting with all of the others. In the tetrahedron of Figure 8:3, the president or managing function is shown as a point at the center which is directly tied to each of the four primary func-

---

[3] The tetrahedron is the fundamental unit of structure in the universe. Its apexes represent the minimum points from which the degrees of freedom may be fixed to describe a single point in space. (A concept developed and demonstrated by Buckminster Fuller—unpublished papers.)

tions located at the corners of the base and apex. Such a chart places research in proper perspective with the rest of the organization. By the nature of its function, research should report at the highest levels in an organization.

If the research organization is relatively small, the director will have research groups, the leaders of which report directly to him. If the organization is larger, those reporting directly to the research director will mostly be heads of individual laboratories. This all may seem very ordinary, even trite; however, there is more here than at first meets the eye.

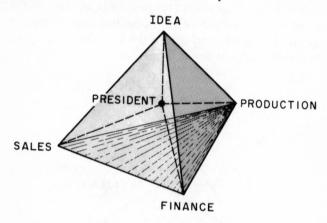

Fig. 8:3 THREE-DIMENSIONAL ARRANGEMENT OF INTRA-
ORGANIZATIONAL RELATIONSHIPS

Only the research and development that is directly related to a particular product or group of commercial products should report to a production manager. All other research should report directly to top management. Captive production research has a tendency to become short-range and ingrown. For the long pull it would be better to err on the side of having too little rather than too much of it. Most researchers, even in independent research groups, are easily enough induced to work on short-term production problems where the objective is specific and the returns obvious.

All of this presupposes that one of management's aims is to get the most effective research for the money. At any given time, however, management may focus on some other objective. It might, for example, have personnel problems which it seeks to alleviate with status symbols—say, by adding a research unit. Such objectives, of course, properly relate to industrial relations, not to research.

The other important factor that is involved becomes evident when we examine the nature of a pyramid. A pyramid gains its rigidity from the fact that the points or corners of its base are joined together. In such a structure, as more compression force is impressed on these points, the more tensile force must be exerted between the basal points to keep them from separating, and the whole unit from collapsing. In like manner, a pyramidal organizational structure involves relationships among the three, four, or more points at the base, as well as between each point of the base and the apex. The planned interchange of communications between the functions represented by the basal points are an essential part of a good organizational structure.

Equally important, or perhaps more so, is the structure established within research to divide responsibility and accountability. In large research groups this is an important factor. As Sherman Kingsbury[4] points out, the research can be divided according to disciplines (chemistry, physics, engineering, etc.), or by class of product (plastics, metals, pharmaceuticals, refrigeration, etc.). In pure research, the division is apt to be by scientific discipline, as for example, in a university department. Industrial research, by contrast, a more natural division, is by product fields. The several factors have been extensively discussed in the above reference.

Dual Channels

The preceding simple statement is about all that need be said about the flow chart of a research organization. The more important parameter, so far as the effect of organization on efficiency is concerned, is the effectiveness of the substructure and of the informal relationships and cross communications. This is so important that in large organizations it may be desir-

---

4 Sherman Kingsbury, *Handbook of Industrial Research Management* (edited by Carl Heyel), Chapter 3; Reinhold Publishing Company, New York, 1959.

able to bring peers from different parts of the research organization together in committees to encourage and increase the opportunity for horizontal communications. Either through semiformal committees tied in at the staff level or through an "open door" policy at the top, there should always be at least two avenues of communication. In this way the top man is not completely dependent upon facts as reported, possibly colored, by his lieutenants; nor is the idea of any researcher anywhere along the line likely to be passed over merely because some one of his superiors was not enthusiastic about it.

Every formal group has, in addition, informal leadership and communications. Management should plan to make as much use of this as possible. Instead of outlawing it, in a sense, and trying to suppress it, management should plan to use it constructively.

It may well be that the exact nature of the primary organization of the research department is relatively unimportant. This is in no wise true, however, of the substructure of research. The wise research director will give ample attention to the size, makeup, and structure of his research groups or crews. He will give attention to age, to the ratio of trained to untrained workers, the specialties of the group members, their particular aptitudes, and even their personalities.

Any sizable research group should be broken down into work groups of, at the maximum, eight to ten—preferably smaller. This is required not so much as a convenience for supervision, as for the psychological reasons. Somehow, loyalty and a feeling of identification becomes much more real and effective when directed to a small group. The attitude that an individual has toward his work "crew" is usually the attitude that he will have for his job and even for the company itself.

Age of Group

One factor that is often considered important is the average age of a given research group. Many statistics have been brought forward to show that important discoveries are usually made by young men. Laboratory heads are encouraged to get rid of the "old" men, namely, anyone over thirty-five. There are reasons to doubt the completeness of the analysis by which this conclusion has been reached. For example, one of the important factors in creativity is the breadth and depth of the store of the individual's knowledge and experience. Certainly the young graduate just out of school is not superior in this. It may be that young researchers so often make important discoveries merely because they chose or are assigned to the newest fields. These are precisely the places where outstanding new discoveries are most easily made.

Take, for example, the young physicist who joined an industrial laboratory to become an electron microscope expert at the time that instrument first became available. Within two years he had developed a new technique which was widely acclaimed. Did this prove that his youth made him more inventive than others in the organization who were fifteen or twenty years his senior, but who were not assigned to "play around" with this new tool? They were considered too valuable in fields where they had been working for some time.

Recent findings indicate that decrease in creativity may result more from motivational and organizational factors than from age. For example, a researcher in his forties or fifties may have attained enough professional recognition and security to have decreased his motivation somewhat. Moreover, he will probably have been assigned some supervisory responsibility and will be serving on some committees. All this takes time and attention from creative thinking. And finally, he will have concentrated on one field and type of problem for so many years that his thought processes will be in a rut.

Investigations on creativity and productivity in research show more correlation with the length of time the individual has been engaged on a given project in a given research group, than with age. Changing to a new type of problem and a different research team will often mentally rejuvenate a researcher who has lost his creativity.

In a paper given in 1957, Donald Pelz[5] included some results of a study concerning relations with colleagues, by H. A. Shepard of the Massachusetts Institute of Technology. The re-

---

[5] Donald C. Pelz, *Motivation of the Engineering and Research Specialist,* A.M.A. General Management Series 186 (1957), pp. 43-44.

searchers in twenty-one industrial laboratories were ranked by their research executive in descending order of excellence on the basis of several criteria: productivity, creativity responsiveness to challenge, etc. The groups also ranked themselves. The data obtained by Shepard showed that after about eighteen months there was evidence of a continuous decline in productivity of the research groups. Ratings both by management and by members of the research groups themselves showed that relatively new groups (under two years) performed better than groups of three to five years' duration. This was true for older as well as for younger researchers.

If these findings prove correct, they have considerable importance for research management. It means that although attention may still be given to the problem of keeping the average age of the group relatively low, even more attention should be given to shifting men within an organization to keep their creativity high. If creativity can be retained and experience added to it, the middle-aged man will prove to be a highly efficient researcher.

Nontechnical Researchers

Another organizational factor than can considerably influence efficiency in research is division of labor. This topic has implications both for the formal organization and for the work group itself. The top of the organizational structure should include no assistant director or assistant laboratory director who is meant to be an alter-ego of the director himself. Such assistants are only bottlenecks in communications between the director and his group leaders. What often is useful is for the laboratory director, who usually is a technically trained man, to appoint a business manager for the laboratory; someone that would manage the paper work and the staff and routine services of the laboratory. Such a manager may also take charge of personnel problems, especially at the nontechnical level. This frees the director to concentrate on technical problems where he has his greatest competence.

Another type of division of labor is the use of both technical and nontechnical workers in a given research group. The Ph.D. chemist who sits by the hour and watches a simple Vigreaux still in operation is not very productive. True, the still needed watching so that appropriate action could be taken if bumping became too violent; but what a waste for a trained researcher to be doing this kind of work. The distillation should have been done by a skilled technician while the researcher applied his mental process to some baffling part of his over-all problem. There are many necessary steps in the performing of experiments that are essentially routine, or require a relatively low order of skill. Such tasks can effectively be done by a laboratory assistant. Workers can be hired who are high-school graduates with a major in science, or who perhaps had a year or two in a junior college.

On the other hand, it is not a satisfactory solution merely to farm out all such tasks. The researcher needs to be close enough to the work to be able to see the actual progress of the experiments that are being run. Sometimes, important insight is gained from observing the behavior during the actual run. The most detailed reporting by an assistant is no substitute for actual observation. A good compromise would have the trained researcher's desk in his laboratory but have him supplied with as much nontechnical help as he can effectively use.

An Idea Man

A final type of division of labor is of utmost importance. Every laboratory should have at least one "idea man". One prolific idea man is probably enough, and more may be too many. A laboratory with several idea men will find itself riding off in all directions at once, most of the time. The term "idea man" is used here to designate a researcher in whom creative thinking is almost an obsession. He will come up with more new ideas in a week than a whole laboratory could examine in a year. Many of his ideas will be bizarre, but he will have an aptitude for thinking of the unexpected. Occasionally, he will come up with a real gem. No laboratory will be as efficient as it might be unless it has an idea man.

The R&D Team

Much is heard these days about the "team approach" to research. This technique of organizing the task can be applied skillfully or indifferently. If a team is to be successful, the members must be carefully chosen. It is generally recognized that there should be diversity. On a chemical research project the group might well include a couple of chemists—probably with different specialties—a physicist, and an engineer or two. But the "Operations Research" boys generally go all out. They are apt to include a pure mathematician and a philosopher, along with a scientist from each of the normal disciplines, including psychology.

Quite as important as diversity of training is the matter of individual personality traits. Paluev suggests that by selecting the members of a group so that all the important faculties of a genius are included, the group can approach the accomplishment of genius. All of this indicates that the team should be created for the problem, rather than merely assigning the problem to some group that happens to be available. In establishing and selecting the members of a research team, the research director is performing an important part of his function.

Along with or perhaps through the team approach, management can rotate researchers into new fields, even into different laboratories, and thus keep interest and creativity high. The new group with a definite, important, assigned objective will quickly weld into a smooth, effective, cooperative team. Once the objective has been attained, the team may be disbanded and the members reassigned to other groups. This applies the psychological trick of using repeated shorter-range objectives to sustain a high level of interest over a longer interval.

Someone is sure to raise the controversial question, "Can a team create?" Would not the same persons working individually accomplish as much, maybe more? The very question reveals a lack of understanding of the way a creative team works. The group members do the actual thinking and conceiving of ideas, even while engaged in the team approach. What is important is that at times the team does sit down together to try to find the best solution to some phase of the problem. During such periods a thought by one may spark an idea for another, and this starts a new train of thought for the third. Thus, the contact of the group stimulates ideas. No one seems ever to object to having a team on a football field merely because only one player carries the ball at a time. Some persons are individualists both at work and at play. Naturally, they should not be forced into team activity. Lydia Strong[6] sums it up nicely in these words:

> A group cannot, obviously, confer on its members greater technical or intellectual abilities than they already possess. It probably cannot increase innate creative ability. But it can, for some persons at least, stimulate the creative process and step up the level of performance.

Let us take note of one additional factor. Competition is generally a very potent motivational force. For this reason many would like to see competition applied in research. This is sound, and wise research management will plan to have some intraorganizational competition. At times, such competition will seem to include duplication but it can, in spite of this, add to over-all efficiency and results. Such competition should be restricted to projects or areas where the return is worth the extra cost. Even as the competition progresses, management can be assembling the advances from each group, and thus, in a sense, leapfrogging the advance. This sort of planned, refereed competition is quite different from having a multiplicity of research directors, all of whom are trying to undercut one another.

---

[6] Lydia Strong, Creativity in industry: The care and feeding of new ideas, *The Management Review,* page 68, March 1957.

chapter 9

MORALE AND MOTIVATION

The directing of research involves primarily working with people. As people have free-will which they use to make choices, their behavior is more complicated and less predictable than that of the physical realm. It is true that human reactions tend to follow certain patterns and are somewhat predictable, but the rules are often different from what would be expected from physical analogy. For example, if I have a picture and give it to you, only one of us has the picture; but if I give you an idea, then we both have the idea. In the physical world, we expect unlikes to attract and likes to repel; but individuals are attracted to those with whom they have much in common.

These and many other observations about human reactions indicate that success in human relations requires learning the rules of practical psychology and applying them. This is doubly important to the supervisor of research workers, whose morale and motivation are so important to good results. In this, the technically trained director of a laboratory has a special problem. Years of training have conditioned him to apply logic in attacking problems, and he has to learn that the same kind of logic does not work with people. To discuss the whole field of practical psychology would take us too far afield, but morale and motivation are so vital to good research performance that they require attention.

MORALE

One of the byproducts of organization and the way it is managed is morale. Military leaders and students of management have long recognized the importance of good morale. They have not always agreed on the best way to build it. High morale is important for any organization, but it is doubly important for research which depends so fully on creative thinking. In this type of work, poor morale not only has a negative effect on the will to accomplishment, but also is a subtle inhibitor to creative ideas.

In seeking to increase efficiency in research, the director will want to give careful attention to the factors that can improve morale. Nor will he have far to look. There are many factors, both on job and off the job, in the home, and in the work group, which contribute to or destroy good morale. Some of them are within the sphere of management control and some of them are outside of it. Some important factors have only recently been discovered. That there are others still unrecognized is highly probable. A number of organizations[1] are conducting extensive research on problems of morale and motivation. As these researches give new insight, supervisors will be better able to manage people wisely.

Often overlooked are the off-the-job factors. These include home, hobbies, friends, organizations, schools, recreation, climate, and even the size of the community. Managers have long known that a man does not leave his home worries or community problems and frustrations at the gate when he comes to work. This is no less true for the researcher. Moreover, he is *expected* to take his daytime problems home with him. If he does not do so, he will surely be less creative than he could be. One of the effective ways to use *illumination* (see Chapter 3) is to sleep on the problem. Hence, all of these off-the-job relationships and factors can affect one's efficiency in research.

---

[1] Such as: Institute for Social Research, University of Michigan; Department of Industrial Administration, Yale University; School of Industrial Management, Massachusetts Institute of Technology; New York State School of Industrial and Labor Relations, Cornell University; Institute of Industrial Relations, University of California.

Environmental Factors

It is not possible to propose an ideal type of community. Some persons are happy only in a large city; others want the informality of suburban living; and a few prefer the "wilds". What is important is that each researcher find friends and recreational activities in the community to meet his needs and those of his wife and family. His home and community environment should be reasonably void of tensions and emotional disturbances.

To improve environmental factors, many companies in smaller communities assist in creating recreational and cultural facilities. Others establish laboratories at locations that have desirable climate or other advantages. All this may contribute to efficiency, or it may be carried to the point where it is actually a hindrance. As is so often the case, moderation is the magic key. Workers can become so involved in extracurricular activities that these even intrude into the thought processes during the day. California is sometimes thought of as an ideal place for a laboratory because of its very favorable climate. On this subject, a wise man countered that because of the fine climate the researchers would get less work done; that in a more rigorous climate they would stay inside and work at least part of the year.

Along this same line, Dr. D. D. Irish relates this experience. He had attended a conference in the East and had met an old classmate. This was a great surprise because this classmate, years before, had settled in Hawaii. When asked what brought him to the States, the classmate replied: "I have moved back. I found it too easy to vegetate in Hawaii and I was too young to want to do that." Yes, an environment can become so comfortable that it soothes the individual into complacency.

Carl Pacifico[2] in discussing creativity said:

> Since no one is ever completely happy or unhappy, creative effort must be associated with some need where the individual is now unhappy. In those areas of human existence where the individual is happy, there is no incentive for new pathways. This effort will be made only to solve a problem. I believe a

---

[2] Carl Pacifico, For creativity—ignorance helps, *Chem. Eng. News,* page 54, May 12, 1958.

moderate amount of friction, within a man and with his associates, is a spur to creativity. Where there is only sunshine,
there is a desert.

There is no formula by which management may decide the
precise balance between too little and too much paternalism.
Most managers in these days seem to err on the side of too
much. Many research leaders have become so conscious of the
factors leading to a relaxed environment that they fail to apply
enough pressure in the way of deadlines to help arouse the disturbed state that must precede creativity.

In examining the factors that enhance on-the-job morale,
two types are evident. One has to do with the organizational
and operational effects on morale, and the other is concerned
directly with motivation. Although motivation and morale are
not separate and distinct factors—they are, in fact, highly
interrelated—it will be convenient to discuss them separately.

Morale Starts at the Top

Good morale in any organization must start at the top. If
the top man interests himself in the problem of morale, his
lieutenants will also do so, right down the line. If the top man
is indifferent to the intangible factors in human relationships,
so will it be with middle management. Moreover, the top man
must translate his interests into action. He will want to keep
his key men fully informed on company plans and policy. He
will want to ask the assistance and suggestions of key men in
making decisions on policy and operations that affect the organization; and he will require his key people also to apply
good techniques in their management of personnel. To this end
he will see that supervisors are trained in how to handle personnel problems. Then he will ask questions about activities
and results in the human relations field often enough to keep
his supervisors convinced that he is interested in the way they
handle this part of their job.

Participation

Experiments have shown that the participation of workers
in decisions regarding the work situation can pay big dividends
both in morale and in output. In one such project, scientists at

the Research Center for Group Dynamics[3] set up a controlled experiment in conjunction with a company that manufactured clothing. When changes in style occurred, new job descriptions had to be developed. Customarily, workers resisted the changes and productivity dropped. Production would then stay down until management reshuffled the entire work force. Along with lower production, morale went down and quitting, absences, and grievances increased.

Under the controlled experiment[4], the next time a change in style occurred three different groups were formed and treated as follows:

Group A received the usual treatment at the change-over. They were called in, the need for the change was explained, and the new rates announced.

Group B had "representative participation" in decision-making. The group was called together and asked to select representatives to set up the new jobs and the new rates. These representatives worked with the engineers on all the details and reported back to the group.

Group C had "total participation." The entire group sat down and worked out the job changes needed. They worked with the engineer in setting the pay rates and job standards.

The standard rate of production for these groups had been sixty. After the change, the job descriptions and rates that were evolved were approximately the same, and everything was approved by the engineer. The results, however, were quite different in the three groups:

Group A, which followed the customary procedure, showed a drop in production from sixty to fifty units, and stayed there. Morale deteriorated; absences and quitting increased. Eventually, the group had to be broken up.

Group B, which had representative participation, returned to a level of sixty units of production in about two weeks. Morale improved; absences and quitting were much less than in Group A.

Group C, in which total participation was used in setting the group objective, showed no drop at all in production. Within

---

[3] A part of the Institute for Social Research, University of Michigan.
[4] The Foundation for Research on Human Behavior: *Creativity and Conformity —A Problem for Organizations,* page 22 (Report on meeting, April 1958).

a short time it had climbed from sixty to seventy units, and stayed there. There was no quitting, and morale was very high. The scientists concluded:

> Group pressures worked in all of these groups, but in one case the group goal held production down, and in the other groups the group goal pushed it up.[5]

In preparing for their experiment, the scientists discovered a dramatic example of group pressure on productivity. In one case they found that:

> The standard rate of production for the pressing department was fifty units per hour. A new girl was hired and, after several weeks, she reached the standard rate of fifty and went slightly above it. The records of the foreman indicated that "scapegoating" began almost at once. (The girl's sewing was tipped off the table, among other things.) Her production rate dropped back below fifty immediately. Shortly after this, her work group was broken up and she continued her old job alone. Her rate jumped to ninety and stayed there.[6]

Effect of Pressures

During the course of studies on pressures for group conformity, researchers found that the presence in a group of one or more individuals with rank and position increased the pressures for conformity. Once a senior has expressed himself, those junior to him hesitate to express any opinion that is different. One technique for minimizing this type of conformity is to arrange to have the junior members express their opinions first. Even this never fully frees an individual of junior years or rank from caution in the face of seniors or superiors.

These group pressures are greater than is generally supposed. At the very most, one would expect that juniors would merely keep silent when they disagree with a view or judgment expressed by one of superior rank. Tests show, however, that in many cases the pressures for conformity are so great that the individual will actually state a position that he does not really hold, just in order to conform.

Pressures for group conformity can be a help or a hindrance to creativity. To orient it constructively, research management

---

[5] *Ibid.*, page 25.
[6] *Ibid.*, page 22.

can take certain actions. Groups can be formed with creativity and new ideas as a specific goal. Procedures can be followed that encourage a full hearing of minority opinions. Difference in status can be reduced or camouflaged. Groups can be formed that bring together diverse kinds of people—a condition that fosters originality. Groups can also be alerted to the consequences of pressures to conform and be assisted to reduce these pressures.

These and other researches show that management-by-participation leads to higher morale. In research organizations it should not be hard to make extensive use of the participation technique. Much of the time it will involve personal conferences between the laboratory director and his project leaders. The project leaders will have ample opportunity to get participation from the project group. For best results, emphasis on participation leadership had better be preceded by some training. Supervisors and group leaders should know how to guide group discussion, draw out ideas and suggestions, and how to reach a consensus without taking undue time.

Training is needed to convince the supervisor, as well as to teach him techniques. There will be no success from the supervisor who says, "Well, OK, I'll lead, but by George, they had better follow." Well-planned, well-led discussion meetings can be—in fact, will be—short, but they can effect maximum efficiency in communications. Participative leadership does not mean that the supervisor sheds his responsibility. Sometimes he will get true group decisions; sometimes he will have to decide, himself. To the extent, however, that they really participate, the group will feel included and involved; and the supervisor will have full advantage of any ideas and information that the group can contribute.

Co-workers

Recent researches in social psychology have shown positive correlation between certain types of on-the-job associations and creative results. Thus, it appears that there are very subtle factors that should be considered in any attempt to maximize morale and motivational forces. Not surprisingly, there is a correlation between the researcher's interests and his performance.

In one study, scientists were asked to fill out a questionnaire. Part of the questionnaire listed nine factors that might be important to their job. The researchers were to indicate how much importance they attached to each. Those that stressed the use of present abilities and knowledge, freedom to carry out original ideas, and contribution to basic scientific knowledge, were considered to have a *science orientation*. Those that laid more stress on having an important job, on association with high-level persons, and on a sense of belonging to an organization with prestige in the lay community, were considered *institutionally oriented*.

These terms become more meaningful when the authors suggest that the science-oriented researcher is one that emphasizes basic research, whereas the institutionally oriented lay more stress on applied research. R. C. Davis, of the University of Michigan,[7] found "that the index of science orientation was significantly related to science performance, whereas the index of institutional orientation was not". In fact, the highest performance was found in those in whom orientation to science was high and institutional orientation was low. Other studies gave the same type of correlation.

Researches reported by D. C. Pelz[8] show the importance of interaction of one researcher with another and with his boss. For example, G. Mellinger compared scientific performance with on-the-job contact with colleagues. He was particularly interested in whether contacts between like or unlike scientists would be most valuable. Similarity or dissimilarity referred to science *versus* institutional orientation of the scientists. The data clearly showed that the highest performance was found when researchers have frequent contact with colleagues that are dissimilar to themselves in values. "Frequent" meant more than several times per week.

When scientific performance was compared with the similarity index of a scientist with his one most important colleague, exactly the opposite correlation was found. High performance

[7] General Management Series No. 186, p. 29; American Management Association, 1957.
[8] Donald C. Pelz, Some social factors related to performance in a research organization, *Administrative Science Quarterly*, Vol. 1, No. 3, December 1956.

paralleled frequent contacts with a like-oriented scientist. Pelz concludes that:

> For maximum performance it is helpful to have at least one close colleague with a similar orientation—someone who "talks the same language", with whom the scientist can air his problems and get a sympathetic hearing. But one or two such individuals are enough. To provide the stimulation of new ideas, it is important that the remaining contacts be with people of dissimilar orientation. In short, one kind of environment for high performance is frequent contact with a variety of viewpoints, a few similar, but most of them different.[9]

Thus, these findings seem to verify the soundness of the idea of the diversified team. They also suggest that the fundamental researcher should not literally be shut off in a corner by himself, but should have contact with engineers and product development scientists. Many contacts of this sort develop quite informally, e.g., at lunch in a company cafeteria. They are obviously important enough, however, that management may not want to leave them wholly to chance.

The Boss

Other studies have examined the relationship between the researcher and his supervisor. Two conclusions seemed reasonably clear from these studies. The first was that leadership seems better able to motivate researchers in proportion as the supervisor himself shows high technical performance and high personal motivation. A leader with a weak flame is not likely to kindle a white-hot flame in others. These results serve as a partial answer to the question whether it would be better to place a business manager at the head of a laboratory, because most scientists have little interest in, and often as little aptitude for, personnel and business problems. The indications are that for reasons of morale and motivation, the laboratory director should be a respected technical man. Of course, as mentioned earlier, he can have a nontechnical assistant to handle the business details.

The second indication from these studies shows something about how a research director should direct. The researcher-supervisor relationship was examined to see what degree of

---

[9] *Ibid.*, page 319.

freedom the researcher had for making his own decisions in selecting work and interpreting results. The range extended from very little freedom to almost complete freedom. According to Pelz, the correlations show that there is fairly clear evidence that participatory leadership is more effective than directive leadership, and also slightly better than the *laissez-faire* pattern.[10]

MOTIVATION

When attention is turned specifically to motivation, it, too, proves to be a complicated problem. It is influenced by organizational structure and by other factors. Organization may be thought of as the body which houses the spirit—motivation. A well body helps, but it does not guarantee a buoyant spirit. In the area of motivation, more attention has probably been given to financial reward than any other single factor. There is no doubt that this is a primary motivating force, naturally more so for some persons than for others.

Bonuses and reward-incentive systems are sometimes used to try to increase financial motivation. These schemes have some merit but they run into certain inherent difficulties. As modern research generally is a group effort, or at least is advanced by important assists from several colleagues, it is often difficult, if not impossible, to appraise equitably the contribution of each researcher to any particular project. Rewards that are not considered equitable by the work group—who sometimes sense more accurately than the supervisor the relevant contributions of each—will damage morale more than they will motivate.

Nevertheless, promotions and salary increases should make it clear that management is aware of who is creative and effective, and does reward performance, rather than seniority. The financial factor becomes an irritant when uniform raises are given with no distinction for performance.

Even a wisely administered salary program has its limitation as a motivational force. It is inherently self-defeating. As a researcher is more highly rewarded financially, money has less and less interest for him. As the economist would say, "The

---

[10] *Ibid.*, page 325.

marginal utility of the next dollar diminishes for him." This rule applies for all of us but is especially true for most scientists, because if money and the status it can buy were not relatively less important to the scientist, he would have entered some other field.

The problem of motivation begins to come into focus when we examine some of the results from recent researches. Studies by Abraham Maslow of Brandeis University have led him to some new concepts. He concludes that by nature man is a *wanting animal;* as soon as one need is satisfied, another appears in its place. This process is unending. Moreover, human needs are organized with certain priorities—a hierarchy of importance.

We can recognize the following types of needs, ranked in order of importance from the bottom upward, to indicate that the bottom one is underlying and most fundamental:

> 5. Self-fulfillment
> 4. Egoistic needs
> 3. Social needs
> 2. Safety needs
> 1. Physiological needs

In general, the needs at any given level have little motivational force until the needs at lower levels have been met, at least in part. Moreover, once the needs at any level are fulfilled, they cease to motivate. "A satisfied need is not a motivator of behavior."

Actually, several of these levels of needs, particularly the upper three, may overlap considerably in their motivational stimuli. They are not mutually exclusive. It is really the ease —or, more accurately perhaps, the completeness—of fulfillment that follows the order from the bottom up.

Physiological Needs

The physiological needs are the most basic and fundamental of man's wants. When these needs are wanting, they become of first importance. For example, consider the need for air. Normally, we give no thought to this need; but for the individual who is under water for a minute or so, the urge for survival causes the need for air to become so dominant that he frantically concentrates his total effort on getting to the surface for a fresh breath of air. The physical needs take precedence until they are met; and once met, they cease to motivate.

Need for Safety

As soon as hunger, thirst, and the other physical needs are satisfied, they cease to be of particular interest. Because man is a rational animal, however, he likes to assure himself that he can continue to meet his physical needs. In modern society this goes beyond the mere assurance of food for the morrow. It includes requirements for shelter and the normal comforts that constitute modern living. These become the second most important driving force that motivates the individual. Whereas the actual physical wants are short-lived but recurring, these needs for safety are often much more enduring. The individual may be some years in realizing the kind of house (shelter) that he feels he requires. His safety for himself and family will require savings, life insurance, and other sizable investments.

Every employee finds himself in a dependent relationship. For him, meeting his safety needs is concerned primarily with security in his job and perhaps promotions to better-paying jobs. Any arbitrary action by management, or any behavior that arouses uncertainty with respect to the job, or any action by management that reflects discrimination or unpredictable administration of policy, are threats to stability and the meeting of safety needs. These factors can be powerful motivators for employees at every level from line worker to vice president. If security is threatened too much, the worker is disturbed to the point where his work suffers. By contrast, if security seems guaranteed and the whole work situation becomes too comfortable, this need ceases to motivate and some workers will produce below capacity.

Social Needs

When man's physiological needs are satisfied and when he is confident that they will continue to be met, his social needs become important motivators of behavior. Under "social" should be listed *the need to belong*, to have association with and acceptance by others, and the giving and receiving of friendship and love. Most of the worker's social needs will be met outside the job, but for best results, it is important that the social contacts on the job also furnish satisfactions for the individual. This does not mean that there will not be pressures, as between worker and boss, or even between competing workers. It does mean, however, that the individual receive recognition as a worthy member of society; that he be accepted by the group on an informal basis for his own personal contribution.

In the socio-economic relations of the job situation, a failure to satisfy a personal need leads to undesirable behavior which is contrary to the objectives of the organization. These reactions often appear to have no basis, or at least no connection with the basic cause. In acute cases, physical illness can develop from psychosomatic causes. More generally, however, if satisfaction of social needs and safety needs is thwarted, the individual will become resistant, antagonistic, and uncooperative. He will subconsciously, and sometimes consciously and intentionally, direct his efforts counter to the objectives of the organization.

Egoistic Needs

After the more fundamental needs of physical wants, safety, and social acceptance have been met, at least in part, the egoistic needs become chief motivators. These are of two kinds:

1. Those needs that relate to one's self-esteem, which may be characterized as the need for self-confidence, for independence, for knowledge, and achievement.
2. The needs that relate to one's reputation, which we might characterize as needs relating to recognition, appreciation, and respect.

Whereas the needs of the lower order are often rather completely satisfied in our industrial society, these egoistic needs are rarely if ever satisfied. Once this type of need becomes the motivating factor, there appears to be an infinite variety of ways in which the need reasserts itself for repeated satisfactions. This is the level at which much of the motivation of a research worker will be found. Attempts to motivate him at the lower levels may arouse fears and distract from his creativity.

Needs for Self-Fulfillment

Allied with, but also above and beyond, the egoistic needs, are the needs for self-fulfillment. The needs for the individual to realize his own potentialities for continued development and for creative contributions of the highest order. Chris Argyris [11] has listed seven ways in which the normal individual finds continuing need for personal growth. This need for growth and development in personality is the least tangible of all motivational need, and is precisely most effective in stimulating creative workers with their high order of ideational ability. This is probably the area in which the most creative individuals find their motivation. This is the dominant drive for problem-solving that transcends the mere reward of money or personal acclaim. This is an area in which the gifted individual can demonstrate his superior talent—a means whereby he wins for himself a sort of nobility that cannot be bestowed by mere man.

If these concepts truly reflect human motivational factors, they have some important implications for management, and especially for research management. They raise provocative questions concerning knotty problems of salaries, titles, and promotions. By paying good salaries and building confidence in security on the job and by adding many fringe benefits, management has deprived itself of motivators on which conventional theory has taught us to rely—namely, rewards, promotions, or threats and other coercive devices. The carrot-and-stick theory looks good on paper. The stick here refers primarily to the threat of loss of job, and hence, the jeopardizing of the physiological and safety needs. So with satisfied workers, management must turn primarily to the carrot for motivation. Management cannot provide a man with self-respect, nor with the esteem of his fellows, nor with self-fulfillment, but it can create conditions that encourage and enable him to

---

[11] Chris Argyris, *Personality and Organization*, Harper & Brothers, New York, 1957.

seek such satisfactions *for himself,* or it can thwart him by poor policies and "plant rules."

Theory Y

As a result of researches on motivation and as a means of summarizing and recognizing these results, Professor Mc-Gregor[12] formerly in the School of Industrial Management at M.I.T., has proposed a theory. He has come to believe that many practices of management have found acceptance because of a false premise about human nature and motivation. Consequently, he has proposed a new theory of the task of managing people based on more adequate assumptions. He has called his proposal "Theory Y." In a sense, McGregor has proposed a rationale for orienting the individual's goals so that they advance the objectives of the organization in much the same way as competition and free markets match the individual's self-interest to the needs of society.

"Theory Y" proposes that:

1. Management is responsible for organizing the factors of production: ideas, money, materials, tools, and people.
2. People are not by nature passive or resistant to organizational objectives. They often have been made to behave in a passive or antagonistic way by poor management procedures.
3. The potential for development of competence, the motivation for constructive activity, the capacity for assuming responsibility, the willingness to direct behavior toward organizational goals, are all present in people. Management does not put them there but can thwart them or can encourage and make it possible for people to recognize and develop these natural characteristics.
4. The essential task of management is to arrange organizational structure, plant rules, and procedures so that people can achieve their own goals *best* by directing *their own efforts* toward the organization's goals. This means, among other things, a genuine respect for workers as individuals, and *participative management.* As Peter Drucker has called it, "management by objective" and not "management by control".

---

[12] D. M. McGregor, *The Human Side of Enterprise;* McGraw-Hill Book Company, New York, 1960.

Management by Objective

Management by objective is being given increased consideration by alert management. Some companies are trying the approach of having the individual set targets or objectives for himself and in having him self-evaluate his performance on a semiannual or annual basis. These and other devices can be used by research directors to assure better motivation of the researcher on his particular project, and to increase his cooperation with other researchers on the general objectives of the organization.

Older theories of management were based on the assumption that man is by nature passive and lazy, and will insofar as possible shun the activity known as "work." Theory Y assumes that it is more realistic to think of man as an active creature; that, in fact, complete inaction is a pathological condition. Both humans and test animals will engage in physical exertion—even purposeless exertion—by choice after extended periods of inaction.

Granted all this, it is also true that exertion beyond some point is distasteful and is avoided except under adequate motivation. Moreover, experience teaches that once a specific objective is established, man will seek to attain the goal with the least effort. If the objective is to cut some wood, an ax will not be used if a power saw is at hand. If exercise is the objective, however, the ax may be used, but in this case the objective is different.

Apparently the human body does require some physical exercise to maintain proper functions and well-being. Beyond this, effort must be stimulated by some motivational force, especially if the effort is to be directed with continuity to a specific objective. Such activity carries with it the desire to produce maximum results—to reach the goal with the least effort.

Perhaps even more important than any inner urge for physical activity is an urge for mental activity for making decisions. This is evident in many ways; daydreaming and worry are two examples. The wide appeal of games of chance, where every event invites a new judgment; the appeal of high-scoring or fast-action sports is another indication. How much spectator-appeal is there in a slow-moving game of chess? It appears that once a decision or commitment has been made, man seeks to accomplish it with least effort so as to get on to the more interesting event of making a new decision or commitment.

This explains in part the value of participative management. The activity that is really endemic is the process of deciding—setting the objective—and the worker that has participated in this has a commitment which sheer need for some physical exercise does not give him.

Delving deeper into the motivating process gives more insight into the effective management of creative workers. To speak of *motivating someone* is really not accurate. Motivation is a personal, an internal, state. At best, the stage can only be set so that the individual is more inclined to be self-motivated. The anchor point of motivation is the individual's self-image. If the particular activity or objective is viewed by the individual as being consistent with—or, in fact, as reinforcing—his self-image, he will be motivated to action. If the individual views the relation between the requirements of the job and his self-image as weak or negative for him, his reaction will be indifference or antagonism. For example, if the individual thinks of himself as being intelligent and believes that successful accomplishment of a given task indicates superior intelligence, he will be motivated to give it a hard try. By contrast, if an individual views a given job as being routine and repetitive, and prides himself as being creative, he will not be happy in the job nor motivated to give it his best. Another person who views himself as being good at details might be challenged by the job.

Participative management, or getting a researcher to think of a project and propose it, himself, involves this factor of the self-image. The individual that proposes an idea or objective has already committed himself. This automatically aligns the project as positive to his self-image. The individual's decision is at stake and he is motivated to act so as to prove the validity of his judgment. The orientals call this "saving face."

Fortunate is the director that has researchers whose self-image involves the idea of creativity. The wise director will try to build as much of this attitude as he can. The whole research organization, including administration of recognition and rewards, should build creativity and innovation into a symbol of status. Having taken account of the self-image of each researcher, the director will then need to help the researcher to see as much as possible of positive relationship between this and the given project.

One factor in motivation that cannot be overworked is the idealistic urge. All of us desire to be constructive and useful. Most everyone, especially in his youth, would like to do something noble for humanity, and this trait should be capitalized. Alert research management will be quick to point out the social values of the problem in hand. Unassisted, the researcher may not equate social service with the profits or savings that an invention or discovery may bring to his organization. Yet, as was pointed out in Chapter 6, potential profit is the best over-all measure of social usefulness. The supervisor of research should never tire of pointing out the importance of research, and, in fact, the particular project at hand, in advancing our standard of living.

In doing this he can enumerate four ways in which research can lead to greater satisfaction of human desires and needs. A creative idea may:

1) Create a new function (examples of this sort extend all the way from the spectacles to television);
2) Improve an existing function—the commonest research objective and contribution;
3) Develop greater economy—a cheaper process or method of construction;
4) Increase salability, which gives artistic satisfactions and enhances distribution, better competitive position, and, indirectly, saving through increased production at incremental costs.

All will agree that motivation requires a highly personalized approach. The thoughts that have been called to attention here are intended merely as suggestive of some areas to consider and some techniques that can be applied in the appropriate situation. The problem of motivation is at the core of the problem of *how* a research director should direct the research. Effective handling of the human relations problems of the laboratory can contribute importantly to the efficiency of the research group.

chapter 10

COMMUNICATIONS

That communication is important is generally agreed. The question is: How much and what kind will be advantageous? The expansion of coffee breaks and group celebrations of holidays, birthdays, retirements, weddings, and even births, has caused some to wonder if informal communications have not usurped first importance. Nevertheless, on-the-job sociability, in moderation, is important because of its contribution to morale. In looking at communication and its effect on research efficiency, however, this discussion will bypass the strictly social contacts and center attention rather on job-related contacts. Further, it will limit consideration to communication within the research groups, and between research and the supporting organization. To be sure, exchange of knowledge and ideas with scientists outside the organization also has some impact, but this concerns a larger field of policy and action than will be considered here.

Within the organization there are two types of communication: formal and informal. In a different dimension there can be listed two purposes of communications: One is for the transfer of information and knowledge; the other is to increase cohesion within a group and feelings of personal security. The first has to do essentially with the intellect; the second, more with feelings.

Formal Reports

Formal communication consists of the written records by the researcher himself and reports by laboratory groups. The formal record begins with the notes, data sheets, diary, etc., which will be kept as a laboratory record on the progress of experiments. These records are vital, not only for knowing and evaluating the course of the experiment but for patents. Naturally, such records should be so complete that the researcher, or in fact any of his colleagues, could reproduce the experiment or check results and calculations from the data recorded. Professor F. E. Bartell, formerly Head of the Physical Chemistry Department at the University of Michigan, used to say: "If the experiment is worth doing, it is worth taking the time to properly record the procedure and the results."

Formal reports will consist of *progress reports* by the researcher, *project reports* when he has completed the project or some phase of it, and *budgetary reports* by the head of the laboratory. The progress and project reports serve a dual purpose: They are useful for informing management of the activities and progress in the laboratory. They are also useful in keeping colleagues within the research organization up to date on the latest developments in different sections of the laboratory. This permits the newest scientific data and information to be utilized within the research organization, and it may also catalyze new ideas on other projects.

The writing of reports takes time from actual research. Excessive report writing will retard research. Communications of progress and results are essential, however, and the writing of a report often assists the researcher to organize his thinking and gain a better perspective of his project. Research management will want to balance the values from communication against the time required for writing reports so as to ensure optimum benefits.

In any sizable research organization, the budget report of the research director or head of the laboratory becomes an important means of communications. This is essentially a selling job. It will evaluate the research in progress, perhaps the results of the previous year, and thereby justify the budget request. A great deal of ingenuity has been applied to the matter of evaluating the results of research. Attempts have been made to relate expenditures for research to corporate growth, for example. This justification of research may well be a necessary evil, but as a project it should not be taken too seriously. Obviously, research must more than pay for itself or, economically, it is not worth doing. The trouble is that on any particular project or in any particular research organization, there is no way to evaluate any particular research contribution. It can be done only on an over-all, long-term historical basis.

A laboratory may well go along for several years making no really worthwhile, tangible contribution and then, in a single project, pay its way for the next fifty years. Two laboratories may operate on similar budgets year in and year out for many years. The one might be very productive with profitable ideas; the other accomplish very little. This is why, as we indicated in Chapter 6, so much attention must be given to selecting and working upon the right problems. The quality of research, so much more than the dollars spent, is the vital determinant. Although research management will continually need to advise top management of the potential of the particular research at hand, little time should be spent in trying to place dollar-and-cents evaluations of research on a short-term basis. The time might better be spent on more research. In general, if management believes in research, justification will not be too hard. If management has doubts about the value of research, the laboratory director has a tough selling job.

Informal Communications

Fully as important as the formal communications is the informal flow of information throughout a research organization and between the researchers and management. The great value to be derived from the informal contacts is the assistance it gives to the creative thinking processes. Who has not had the experience of facing a problem and seeking advice from a colleague, and in the very process of stating the problem found an answer or at least new insight into the problem? Improved creativity and improved morale are desirable products of informal communications.

Committees

The best informal communications are those that occur naturally. Within any laboratory unit such contacts will be adequate unless management interferes with the freedom for such communications. As between different laboratories in a large research organization, it may be desirable to plan for informal contacts—discussion groups and the like. Often, committees appear to accomplish little and are considered a waste of time. In some organizations, excessive committee meetings may leave little time for constructive work. Nevertheless, the judicious use of committee meetings can serve a good purpose in informal communications, and for this purpose, decisions are not essential. Committees can bring together researchers who otherwise would have little contact. If committees were recognized for their major contribution—namely, communications and clarification of objectives and not decision-making— they would be less maligned and better utilized.

The most important of informal communications is that between the laboratory director and his people—between the researcher and his "boss." Research management needs to be very conscious of the value and implications of these contacts. If the researcher does not have satisfactory face-to-face contacts with his chief, he will begin to feel left out and worry about his future and security. It is not enough for the director to stop in the individual's research laboratory and socialize with him occasionally, although he should do this also. The director should find time to call the individual researcher into his office and there discuss with him his project and related matters of interest, including the organization's objectives and policy. Such conferences contribute to the individual's feeling of belonging and they improve his concept of the status of his job and its importance. The director must carefully avoid spending too much time with a few of his researchers and too little time with others. Such lopsided distribution of attention will lead to doubts, fears, and jealousy on the part of those that feel that they are being slighted.

These conferences can and should provide training and inspiration for the researcher. The research director or leader is usually a respected scientist. In addition, he will be acquainted with the organization's objectives and problems. His broader knowledge and backlog of experience can be judiciously used to motivate the researcher and to improve his skill in analyzing problems.

If the research management does a good job of motivating the individual researcher, gives him considerable latitude in carrying out his research project, and if discipline is maintained through judicious deadlines, interested questions on progress and acceptable plant rules, the problem of informal communications will largely take care of itself. It does remain a factor, however, in the over-all effectiveness of a research organization, and if the communications are not satisfactory, it will impede the effectiveness of the group.

chapter 11

EQUIPMENT
FOR RESEARCH

Automation, which has gained so much attention in recent years, has fired the imagination of many researchers. They envision gains in efficiency in research through automation. They talk of push button research. The proper use of automatic instruments and electronic computers may indeed improve efficiency in research, but they will not necessarily do so. To be effective, these aids must be applied to a sound research program. As research is really an activity of the mind and not of the hands, the use of equipment contributes not to the creative part of research but rather to the testing of hypotheses, as set forth in step 4 of Chapter 2. Too much emphasis on the use of gadgets and elaborate equipment may actually increase the cost for a given result.

In any case, to advance efficient research there is need to give careful attention to the question of equipment. Every piece of equipment for research should pass the same economic test as a new piece of plant equipment: Will the equipment pay for itself? One effective way in which the researcher can evaluate a major expenditure is to ask himself whether he would prefer the given piece of equipment to additional manpower. In examining this question, attention will be directed to the laboratory itself, the equipment in the laboratory, and pilot plant operations.

LABORATORY

Many extensive studies on how to design and build modern,

197

efficient laboratories have been reported.[1] The emphasis has generally been on designing for flexibility, for safety, and for logical organization of work. It is not our purpose here to re-examine laboratory design. It will be in order to remind our-selves, however, that a laboratory is a workshop and not neces-sarily a showplace.

A chemist in industrial research had an experience that illus-trates the point. His company had just built a new laboratory and he was assigned appropriate space in the new building. He could not do his research there, however, because he was working with carbon black which would have made the place dirty. In fact, the laboratory director was so proud of the building that anyone that laid a book on the window sill or opened a window more or less than others down the hall was likely to have his attention called to this undesirable conduct. This reminds us of Parkinson's[2] comments on buildings as monuments. If the objective is efficient research and not ad-vertising, then of a certainty the laboratory should be con-ceived, built, and operated as a place in which to do work—albeit a very specialized kind of work. The designer will want to give detailed attention to the type of research to be done and the special requirements for space and for the type of organization.

In considering the laboratory building, these factors should be balanced against costs. The laboratory, first of all, is a shel-

---

[1] *Buildings for Research;* F. W. Dodge Corp., New York, 1958.
Laboratory Design, edited by H. S. Coleman; Reinhold Publishing Company, 1951.
Chemical Business Handbook, edited by John H. Perry, McGraw-Hill, New York, 1954.
Acoustics for the Architect, by Harold Burris-Meyer and Lewis S. Goodfriend; Reinhold Publishing Company, 1957.
Architects' pointers pare building costs, *Chemical Week,* Vol. 81, December 7, 1957, pages 41-50.
Toxic area semi-works, *Chemical Engineering Progress,* Vol. 54, January 1958, pages 49-53.
Laboratories at $12 a square foot, *Chemical & Engineering News,* Vol. 33, August 29, 1955, page 3564.
Emphasis on efficiency, *Chemical & Engineering News,* Vol. 33, May 23, 1955, page 2200.
Laboratory Planning for Chemistry and Chemical Engineering, edited by Harry F. Lewis; Reinhold Book Division, 1962.
[2] Professor C. Northcote Parkinson, *Parkinson's Law;* Houghton Mifflin Company, Boston, 1957.

ter for the personnel and equipment. Not only should the building keep out the weather, but it should also control temperature, summer as well as winter, to reasonable comfort. A second requirement is to arrange convenient services of electricity, air, water, vacuum, steam, and special gases where required. One other important consideration is concerned with the problem of morale. The building itself should be such that the researcher will have a natural pride in his place of work. This does not require an expensive or elaborate building, however. In fact, if the leadership focuses attention on results and efficiency, pride will develop around the idea of economic utility instead of monumental art.

EQUIPMENT

The laboratory equipment comprises the tools with which the researcher tests his ideas. We must interpret this in the broadest sense. Equipment consists of the books in the library, the calculating machines, and the electronic computers, as well as the mechanical equipment. Efficiency in research requires good modern tools, and they are becoming so extensive and expensive that attention must be given to their effective use. Can several groups use the same equipment alternately? Can the work be organized for around-the-clock operation? Can a service group be established with experts to maintain and operate specialized equipment for the whole research group?

This type of efficient use of equipment is rather common in larger research organizations. Human nature being what it is, however, these very techniques for efficiency have some pitfalls. When such services as analyses, distillations, computations, etc., can be had for the asking, the researcher is apt to ask for more than he really needs. He may not think very hard about ways to keep down such costs. Research management will need to apply eternal vigilance and strive hard to motivate against this type of inefficiency.

The importance of evaluating the costs of equipment was brought to my attention by a personal experience. Once when I was operating a rather elaborate set-up of glass equipment, the material in one of the flasks carbonized and the ground glass joint stuck. As I contemplated an extensive disassembly of the equipment, it suddenly dawned on me that I could save time by breaking the flask. A few seconds of mental arithmetic showed that the savings of time would offset the cost of the flask severalfold. It was a real shock to realize that I could make money by breaking a dirty but otherwise good flask.

Equipment that will make a faster, more accurate, or an automatic measurement usually will increase efficiency. Sometimes the substitution of micro for macro equipment proves to be more efficient, but not necessarily so. On the other hand, a custom-built miniature of some proposed plant unit usually gives poor results. It is often impossible to isolate the many variables and obtain meaningful data. It is far better to analyze the problem so as to determine the variables and their behavior. Basic data can then be obtained—usually in quite simple experiments—and from these data engineering calculations will suffice for the design and sizing of commercial equipment. The wise researcher will keep the use of working-scale models to the minimum as they are costly and often leave many unanswered questions.

Research management should train and encourage the researcher to spend more time analyzing the problem and learning about the key variables. The procedure set forth in Chapter 2 was designed to assist in just this phase of research. Emphasis on this approach will lead to more research being done in the head and on paper, with a great saving in time and expense and a corresponding increase in efficiency. The building of equipment should be a sort of last resort or a final testing to convince the skeptical who must see the "wheels go around" to believe.

PILOT PLANTS

The construction and operation of pilot plants is the most costly part of research and development. Pilot plants seldom cost less than $50,000 to $100,000, and often as much as several million dollars. The operation usually requires a crew of men, often on an around-the-clock basis. One of the greatest opportunities for cost reduction in research is in the reduction or elimination of pilot plant operations.

There was a time in the development of the process industries when it was the accepted practice that no plant unit should be built more than ten times the size of proved units. This "rule of ten" meant that each new plant or process had first to be tested in a pilot plant and then in a semiplant before risking capital in a full size plant. This is one of the reasons why many chemical plants in the early part of this century were merely overgrown replicas of the laboratory equipment in which the experiments were first run.

Chemical engineering has made great strides since those days. This branch of engineering has developed many useful empirical equations and has learned how to apply many theoretical concepts in the area of phase rule, kinetics, thermodynamics, heat flow, fluid flow, and the like. As a result of this, the old "rule of ten" has lost much of its relevance. In most cases a good chemical engineer can design and size equipment for the petroleum or chemical industry directly from basic scientific data. For example, all a good chemical engineer needs for design of a commercial still are data such as the composition of the mixture to be separated, the density, viscosity, surface tension, boiling point, and data on liquid-vapor equilibrium for each of the components. From these data he can design a still for any desired through-put and to deliver products of any desired purity.

The possibility of bypassing the pilot plant stage was dramatically demonstrated early in World War II. The Phillips Petroleum Company had signed a contract to build a butadiene plant for the government's program on synthetic rubber. The basic physical-chemical data were carefully measured, and then the engineers designed a full-scale plant. It worked just as designed, and much expense and at least six months of precious time were saved.

In like manner, great advances have been made in other branches of engineering—aeronautical, mechanical, electrical, and electronics. Unfortunately, the social sciences have not yet developed to the point where they even recognize the fundamental difference between science and engineering.[3] This

---

3 *Science* concerns itself solely with observing facts and arranging them into an organized body of knowledge. Science is amoral; it knows neither right or wrong; it respects only truth. *Engineering* concerns itself with applying knowledge to the supplying of human needs. Engineering is constantly faced with moral and economic questions, and with the question of right and wrong.

has led to great confusion in the application of sound principles in the field of political economy.

The potential of modern design engineering has great significance for the researcher. Every researcher should acquaint himself with the engineering design methods in his field. This will help him to plan his experiments for more effective cooperation with the engineer. This, in turn, will reduce the cost of research; and more importantly, it will shorten the lag time until the results can be socially useful.

What, then, are the reasons for building pilot plants? When is the costly expenditure for a pilot plant required? In answering these questions it will be desirable to condition ourselves by substituting the word "excuse" for "reason," because many of the so-called reasons for pilot plants are merely rationalizations for the habit of building them.

It has long been claimed that a pilot plant must be built and run to acquire data for the design of a full-scale plant. This is seldom a valid reason. In most cases a good process or design engineer can do a better job with basic data. In the process industries, for example, equipment for the various types of separations (distillation, extraction, crystallization, etc.) can be designed from data on phase equilibrium and physical constants of the substances involved. In like manner, any requirements for heat exchange can be calculated from basic data and known coefficients. The required basic data may be available in the literature. If not, they can be found quickly in the laboratory, usually with simple and standard equipment. In fact, such physical data should be a key part of the information that the researcher passes on to the engineer.

If the problem involves the design of a reactor, the laboratory will need to give the engineer data on space velocity and contact time along with heat of reaction and pertinent physical data in the temperature range involved. The point is that, in most cases, the data necessary for design can be obtained more quickly and more cheaply in the laboratory on standard equipment or on the miniplant scale.

For certain projects, pilot plants will always be required. These are truly pioneer fields in which engineering techniques have not yet been developed. Design for use of nuclear reactions would surely come in this category. But even then many parts of any process will involve unit operations for which the engineering is well developed. This should be taken into account when a pilot plant is being planned.

Another reason often given for the use of pilot plants is the evaluation of recycle. Shifts in concentration, accumulation of impurities undetected in single runs, and unexpected side reactions often show up for the first time in a continuous run with recycle. This would be a complete and adequate reason for a pilot plant, were it not for the fact that often the same information can be obtained from a continuous miniplant. Such a unit can be set up in the laboratory, usually at a fraction of the cost of a pilot plant. In recent years, instrument makers have developed micro-pumps and metering devices which make continuous operation on a very small scale quite feasible.

Occasionally, a special circumstance may require a pilot plant for full evaluation of some corrosion problem. In most cases, however, test strip of the proposed metals of construction, when placed at key points in a miniplant, will give necessary data for materials selection.

The most valid reason for building and operating a pilot plant is to make material for market testing. The developing of a market may require sizable samples over an extended period. The prospective customer wants to be sure that the product will serve his need and that the quality can be maintained. In some cases this reason alone is justification for building a pilot plant. Careful examination of this question may reveal, however, that for market tests the product can be made in improvised equipment. Even where part of the process may need a pilot plant, other parts may not need to be tied into the unit.

There is another possible reason for a pilot plant—one that is never mentioned. If management has not yet made up its mind to proceed with a given project, it may authorize the moderate expenditure for a pilot plant until it can decide whether to proceed with it, or abandon it. Needless to say, the costs of this pilot plant really should be charged to general overhead and not to research.

Selection of the right problem is the factor that has the greatest influence on efficiency in research by leading to more useful and profitable results. In the actual research itself, the greatest opportunity for saving dollars is in the developmental stage. Here rises the question: To pilot plant or not to pilot-plant? Minimizing development costs will do wonders for the research budget. Application of the procedure for research as outlined in Chapter 2 will emphasize analysis of the problem at hand, and by attacking the fundamentals involved it will reduce the tendency to rely on expensive pilot plants to compensate for incomplete research at the bench.

chapter 12

CONCLUSION

Research and experimentation are the tools for progress. Just as automation has improved efficiency in production, so will better organization, methods, and problem-solving techniques improve efficiency in research and accelerate progress. The large variation in productivity between different laboratories and researchers indicates that efficiency in research can be greatly improved. The rewards, which can be very large, are of two types. One is improved productivity of human effort, and hence, a higher standard of living for society. The other is the deep personal satisfaction that comes from creating a better method. Improvement in the tools, methods, and organization of research means a permanent advance, ensuring a kind of immortality.

Business management must take direct responsibility for productivity from research. In a sense, however, management is only the agent of society. It is society that places the final evaluation on research. Management can organize and motivate, but it is society that establishes the degree of recognition and the scale of rewards. When we note that a hillbilly singer is paid as much for a single performance as an outstanding scientist receives for months of effort, it raises questions about society's set of standards. In the past couple of decades, managements have begun to understand better the value of research. Now they need to communicate that sense of value to the rest of society.

Ideas and Profits

New ideas are the starting point for useful change and progress, but an idea by itself is useless. It must be put to work;

this requires capital. In a society with free enterprise, capital is attracted by profits. If the economic profits from the greater efficiency inherent in a new idea or process are taxed away or passed on to the consumer too completely or quickly, capital will not be attracted to finance full utilization of the idea. In free enterprise, profits are the means by which capital is directed into those processes and goods that represent the greatest increase in efficiency in serving society's needs. Savings utilized as risk capital supply the tools to put ideas to work, and are essential to improving our way of life.

Measuring Efficiency of R&D

Any discussion of effective research sooner or later leads to the question of measuring the results of research. Probably every research manager has wrestled with this problem and without too much success. In understanding the physical world, new insights often follow new ability to quantify the pertinent factors. To try to do so in research is a worthy objective. The difficulty is that no one has found a way to measure satisfactorily the contribution of research, at least on a current basis. Moreover, any contribution from current research will by its very nature be realized only in the future, frequently a distant future. In fact, the more fundamental and valuable the project, the longer will the return usually be delayed. All this poses a very baffling problem in measurement.

One of the usual methods of evaluating research is to relate expenditures to sales. Attempts to show specific time lags between expenditures and sales increases have been disappointing. There is little evidence of a direct correlation between, for example, surges in research and the subsequent increases in sales. Comparison between expenditures for research and growth in sales becomes more meaningful when both are summed for a considerable period of time. It is reported of the Minnesota Mining & Manufacturing Company that from 1926 to 1952 they spent $33,500,000 for research and experienced $950,000,000 in sales of new products. This was primarily the direct result of their expenditures for research and development, and it shows a ratio of 28.5:1 for new-product sales to research. This sort of comparison for "3M" shows an excellent return on the research expenditures over the period. Very probably, such a comparison would show similar results for any company that shows good growth.

Unfortunately, such comparisons relate only to the results of past research. They are applicable to present and possible future research only by indirection. To extrapolate from the past, one must assume that the present research group will match past performance. On a statistical basis this seems like a reasonable assumption. Conditions are apt to change, however. The research organization may become larger, researchers age, the individuals composing the group will change. As a result, the effectiveness of the group may change. It may improve, it may deteriorate, or it may remain constant. It is customary to assume that the efficiency will remain constant or gradually improve. Although such an assumption seems rather plausible, it should be recognized for what it is—primarily, faith.

Comparisons of expenditures for research with capital expenditures have shown no more promise. Companies that have led in expenditures for research have, in general, grown rapidly. This is only true as a statistical average, however, and there would be considerable spread in the data if a careful correlation were made. This follows for two reasons. First, differences in the effectiveness of research will distort the relation between the dollars spent for it and growth. Second, there are many other factors and business decisions that influence growth. Decisions on investments, effective merchandising, pricing policies, and government actions, for example, will importantly influence growth and may reinforce the contribution of research or thwart it.

If, then, statistical comparisons relating to growth primarily report on the past, how can the present be evaluated and related to the future? Upon examination there appear to be two ways to approach the problem of evaluating research. One is the aggregate approach, in which the total results of research are related to the organization's accomplishments. The other is a project-by-project approach. This latter method shows more promise for evaluation of current action. The evaluation of each project and summing to get a total may be more useful in arriving at a level for profitable expenditures than an attempt to set the level directly.

To evaluate a given project, it will prove useful to apply some fundamental concepts. By estimating the savings of the new product or process under consideration, the results of the research can be approximately evaluated. Research management should seek to select projects and approaches to research that maximize these savings and minimize the costs. The ratio of the saving to the cost of the research is the real value of the research.

The procedure outlined is suited to an existing product or process that is to be improved or replaced. With other projects the substitution will be too indirect and involved to permit such a comparison. For these it may be possible to evaluate the project by calculating costs and estimating selling price. Price-quantity charts, such as shown in Figure 6:1, indicate the order of magnitude of the market to be expected at a given price. From the estimated market, selling price, and cost, the profit can be calculated. This gives a measure of the potential profit if it is successfully completed.

After a product has been marketed long enough to have established a growth pattern, it may be possible to estimate the value of the research involved through the savings indicated by the second derivative—∂x^2. As indicated in Chapter 6, the second derivative shows the increment of profit over alternative use of capital.

These methods of evaluating research are, at best, very crude. They may always remain so because of the many variables and steps from the conception of a new idea until it is finally successfully commercialized. Until such time as someone devises a new approach, attempts to measure the effectiveness of research will somewhat resemble tilting at windmills. Instead of spending time trying to measure past results, a good manager will focus on trying to improve efficiency from its present level. He that is running as hard as he can has no time to look back. If the research director keeps management busy commercializing new projects, they will have little time to wonder how good is research.

Examination of the research management problem shows at least six factors that affect efficiency in research and about which management has responsibility. Of primary importance is the selection of problems with substantial potential—those that contribute to increased productivity in meeting society's needs. The selection of researchers and the nature of the organization in which they work become progressively important as the size of the research group increases. Organization, communications, and morale also become increasingly important with size. Proper balance in equipment for research can do much to minimize costs, but this factor needs constant attention because of the fascination that working models and gadgets have for most researchers.

Three other factors that affect over-all research efficiency are:

1) The method of attacking the problem,
2) The effectiveness of "selling" the results, and
3) The training of the researcher.

These factors are controlled by the researcher; he alone can do something about them. Chapters 2, 3, and 4 outline some specific techniques for improving efficiency in these areas. Although these suggestions are directed mainly at the researcher as he is confronted with a problem, the principles are applicable to the solution of any problem.

The Six-Step Method

The research director will find the procedure outlined for solving problems well adaptable to the problems that he faces. He will find, for example, that his first step is to clarify his objective. When he clarifies it he will find that his objective is not to invent, but rather to incite others to invent and develop. The research leader can adapt and apply the systematic problem-solving approach to his problem of interesting the researcher in the project. For good results, in fact, the researcher must become excited about the problem. He must, in fact, arrive at the disturbed state where he actually wants to do something about it. An important part of arousing the "disturbed state" is the creation of a feeling of need. The leader has a good opportunity to do this as he and the researcher jointly discuss the objective of the project. Sometimes a series of shorter-range objectives, which collectively lead to the over-all objective, will stimulate more effectively. When and how to use such techniques is part of the director's job.

The manager's job requires creativity no less than the researcher's. Chapter 3, *Creative Thinking*, has useful suggestions for anyone that does creative work. Here the techniques are identical no matter what field is involved. In similar manner, Chapter 4 on report writing is applicable to reporting on any subject. The techniques are equally applicable for the director of research in reporting the activities of the research organization as for the researcher in reporting on his project.

The question of efficiency in research has not received the attention that it merits. A major step forward can be made by directing attention to the similarities between researchers and others of the human race, instead of focusing on the difference, to the point of classing the research process as a baffling enigma. It is time to apply the scientific approach to the problem of efficient research. Free men with good leadership will invent the better life for tomorrow.

Index

Nontechnical researchers, 170